# WHO INVENTED, DISCOVERED, MADE THE FIRST..?

Kenneth Ireland

RAVETTE BOOKS

© Kenneth Ireland 1988
First published by Ravette Books Limited 1988
Reprinted 1989

Printed and bound in Great Britain
for Ravette Books Limited,
3 Glenside Estate, Star Road, Partridge Green
Horsham, Sussex RH13 8RA
by Cox & Wyman Ltd, Reading
Phototypeset by Input Typesetting Ltd, London

ISBN 1 85304 040 1

# Contents

Introduction      vii

Aeroplane      1
Aerosol      2
Ambulance      2
Anaesthetic      3
Aqualung      4
Aspirin      5
Atomic Power-station      6

Baked Beans      7
Ball-bearings      7
Balloon      8
Ball-point Pen      10
Barbed Wire      11
Barometer      12
Battery      13
Bicycle      14
Braille      16
Brassière – *Bra*      16
Breakfast Cereal      17
Building Society      18
Bus      19

Camera      21
Canned Food      23
Carbon Paper      24
Carpet–sweeper      24
Cash Register      25
Cat's-eye      26
Chewing-gum      27
Chocolate      27
Christmas Card      28
Cigarette      28
Cinema      29
Circus      30
Coffee – *Instant*      30
Computer      31
Crossword – *Puzzle*      32

Dentists' Drill      33
Diesel Engine      33

Dishwasher                                    34
Diving-bell                                   35
Diving-suit                                   35
Duplicating Machine                           36
Dye                                           39
Dynamite                                      40

Elastic                                       41
Electricity                                   42
Electric Blanket                              44
Electric Fan                                  45
Electric Light                                45
Electric Motor                                46
Electric Razor                                46
Electric Torch                                46
Elevator – *Lift*                             47
Escalator                                     48

Film – *Moving Pictures*                      49
Fire Extinguisher                             50
Fluorescent Light                             51
Fountain-pen                                  52
Frozen Food                                   53

Gas Fire                                      54
Gas Mask                                      54
Gas Stove                                     55
Geiger Counter                                55
Gramophone – *Record-player*                  56

Hearing-aid                                   59
Helicopter                                    59
Hotel                                         61
Hovercraft                                    62
Hydrofoil                                     63

Ice-cream                                     64
Insulin                                       65

Jeans                                         66
Jet Engine                                    66

Laser                                         68
Lawn-mower                                    68

Lightning Conductor 69
Lock and Key 70
Logarithms 71

Machine-gun 73
Man-made Fibre 74
Margarine 75
Match 76
Metric System 77
Microscope 78
Microwave Oven 79
Milk Bottle 79
Motor Car 80
Motor Cycle 82
Motorway 82

Neon Light 83
Non-stick Pans 83

Parachute 85
Paraffin – *Kerosene* 86
Parking-meter 86
Pasteurization 87
Pedestrian Crossing 88
Penicillin 88
Petrol Engine 89
Petrol Pump 90
Piano 90
Plastic 91
Pneumatic Tyre 92
Potato Crisp 93
Pressure-cooker 94

Radar 95
Radio 96
Railway 97
Refrigerator 98
Rickshaw 99
Roller-skate 100

Safety-pin 101
Safety Razor 101
Seed Drill 103
Sewing-machine 104

Sponsored Walk                          105
Steam-engine                            106
Steam Turbine                           106
Stethoscope                             108
Submarine                               109
Supermarket                             110

Table Tennis                            112
Telephone                               113
Telescope                               114
Television                              115
Toilet-paper                            117
Toothpaste Tube                         119
Torpedo                                 120
Traffic-light                           120
Transistor                              121
Typewriter                              122

Underground Railway                     125

Vaccination – *Inoculation*             126
Vacuum Cleaner                          127
Vacuum Flask – *Thermos*                129
Video-recorder                          129

Water-closet – *Lavatory*               131

X-ray                                   133

Zip-fastener                            134

# Introduction

If you can invent something which people want, you can become rich and famous – as long as you're lucky.

Clarence Birdseye was such a person – he made 22,000,000 dollars in five years from inventing frozen foods. On the other hand, French tailor Barthélemy Thimonnier, who invented the sewing-machine, made no money at all and died in poverty.

A German engineer, Dr Rudolf Diesel, patented the Diesel engine in 1892, but committed suicide 21 years later because of his lack of money. But if you're in the right place at the right time with the right idea. . . .

Sometimes it happens purely by accident. William Perkin, aged 18, was using some chemicals in his father's garden shed, trying to do something else, when he suddenly discovered he had invented aniline dyes.

John Dunlop got so cross when his little son's tricycle, with solid tyres, was making deep grooves in his garden that he devised the bicycle and car pneumatic tyre.

Christopher Scholes had already invented a machine to number pages in a book when a casual suggestion made him invent the typewriter.

Sometimes just a change of name causes success.

For instance, nobody wanted to know about James Gibb's new game until he started calling it ping-pong (now table tennis).

Sometimes, for no real reason, a disaster becomes a success – like King C. Gillette, who invented the modern razor. Few were sold in the first year, but later he was to become a multimillionaire.

Of course, this book cannot include everything. Nobody knows who invented certain items. Indeed, some were improved by many others over such a long period of time that nobody can be quite sure.

# Aeroplane

The French inventor Félix du Temple designed a
*steam*-driven monoplane which managed to fly for
a second or two in 1874. In Russia, Alexander
Mozhaiski did the same using a British-built
steam-engine on his machine ten years later.

Clement Adler, of France, managed to fly
50 metres in 1890 – the first powered aircraft
not to use a starting ramp to raise it into the
air. In 1894 Sir Hiram Maxim (*see* MACHINE-GUN)
got an enormous steam-driven biplane off the
ground.

None of the aeroplanes, though, could be
controlled properly, or manage to fly very far. The
Wright brothers invented the first true aeroplane
with an internal combustion engine to achieve
controlled and sustained flight.

This successful flight was regarded by the Press
as a huge joke. It took place on the morning of
17th December, 1903, at Kittyhawk, North Caro-
lina, USA, in an aircraft designed and built by
Orville and Wilbur Wright. Orville was the pilot
(and only occupant), and it flew for just 12 seconds
at a height of between 2.3 and 3.7 metres (eight
and 12 ft.). Three more flights were made the
same day, the longest for half a mile.

No matter what the newspaper reporters
thought, by improving the design in less than
five years, Orville Wright flew in France for fifty
miles in October 1908.

The modern aircraft industry was already
under way by then, for a firm called Voisin
Frères, of Billancourt, France, started producing
aeroplanes for sale to the general public in 1906.
The first machine was sold on 30th March, 1907.

1

It was a biplane which looked rather like a box-kite.

## ═══════ Aerosol ═══════

This was invented in 1941 by an American, Lyle Goodhue.

In fact, there are three sorts of aerosol. The sort used for spraying into a space, such as an air freshener, puts out particles which are no bigger than one-fifty-millionth of a millimetre in diameter. Canisters for paint produce a spray with larger-sized particles so that they will stick to a surface. Then there are foams, using bigger particles still, such as fun foam, shaving creams, and so on.

The main ingredient is dissolved in alcohol or, as in the case of antiperspirants, in a chemical called aluminium chlor-hydroxide. This is measured into the can, the valve is fitted, then the 'propellant' – which makes it squirt out when you press on the valve – is forced into the can through the valve under pressure. The propellant can be either a gas or liquid. Then when you press the valve, the pressure forces the contents out again.

## ═══════ Ambulance ═══════

The ambulance dates from 1792. Baron Larrey, Napoleon's personal doctor, was worried about the way in which wounded men were being carried from a battlefield. They were simply put into an open cart and taken away, being jolted all the time over the rough ground.

Baron Larrey took a cart, had special springs mounted into it to make them more comfortable, and then had a cover erected over the top to protect the patients from the weather.

The invention proved to be a success. So in 1796 a special French Army unit was established to remove the wounded from battlefields, equipped with 12 of these 'one-horse flying ambulances'.

It took more than 80 years before anyone thought that civilians might need ambulances, too. The first was used on the streets of Margate, Kent, in 1878 – pulled by hand, and with just one wheel! However, in 1883 one appeared with four wheels, rubber tyres and was pulled by a horse.

The first ambulance to have its own engine – fitted with a Daimler engine – was demonstrated in Paris in 1895, but did not go into use with the French Army until 1900. In the same year France was to see the first civilian motorised ambulance appear.

# Anaesthetic

Before anaesthetics were used, if you needed an operation – perhaps to have an arm or a leg amputated – first you would be given some alcohol to drink to deaden the pain, then you would be fastened down, so that the surgeon could work very fast to cause as little pain as possible while the knife or the saw was cutting through you.

After anaesthetics came into use, a surgeon – or dentist – could at last take more time over operations and so do a much better job.

In 1799 Sir Humphrey Davy, chemist and inventor, suggested using laughing gas (nitrous oxide) for the relief of pain during operations. In 1842 William Clark in Rochester, USA, was the first to make a woman unconscious through breathing in the fumes of ether so that she could have a tooth pulled out painlessly.

In the same year Dr Crawford Long, of Jefferson, Georgia, USA, made a patient unconscious with ether before he removed a cyst from the patient's neck, and then went on to perform more operations in the same way. He had to stop because the local people were convinced he was using sorcery and threatened to hang him if he didn't!

Four years later, though, in 1846, ether was being used in a major operation at the Massachusetts General Hospital, Boston, USA, when Dr Warren removed a tumour from a man's jaw. And in the same year, at University College Hospital, London, Dr Liston performed the first painless amputation of a leg, also using ether.

Then Sir James Simpson, of Edinburgh, decided to use chloroform instead of ether because it was thought to be more pleasant and just as effective, both for operations and during childbirth.

From then on operations without anaesthetic were a thing of the past.

# Aqualung

The diving-suit, with an air line and safety line, was invented in the 19th century, but it was –

and is – cumbersome, especially for underwater
exploration.

Jacques Cousteau, an officer in the French
Navy, tried various sorts of compressed air tanks,
but none of them worked properly. The problem
was that there was no way to control the air
supply to make certain that it was at the same
pressure as the surrounding water. Without that
the lungs of the diver could collapse – because
the deeper into the sea you go, the greater the
water pressure becomes.

Then Emile Gagnan, a control-valve engineer,
invented a valve which could supply compressed
air at exactly the right pressure consistently,
Cousteau fitted it to his equipment, and in 1943
it was able to be used.

Since then, Cousteau's Aqualung, the mask,
gas-tank and special valve unit, has been used
throughout the world, and if instead of
compressed air a mixture of oxygen and helium
is used an aqualung diver can descend to a depth
of about 122 metres (400 ft.) freely. (*See* DIVING-
SUIT).

## Aspirin

For centuries it had been known that the use of
some plants and the bark of a number of trees
could relieve the pain of headaches and rheum-
atism. It was eventually discovered why – they
contained acetyl-salicylic acid.

A German chemist, Karl Gerhardt, discovered
how to produce this acid in 1853, but it was not
until 1899 that Dr Felix Hoffman, of the Bayer
Chemical Company, discovered how to make it

pure enough to use in medicine – and then only on a doctor's prescription. The Bayer Company called it aspirin.

By 1915, aspirin tablets were being sold to the public from chemists' shops in packets of 20, without prescription.

# Atomic Power-station

The atomic, or nuclear, bomb was devised by a team led by physicist Robert Oppenheimer in the USA and was ready for use in 1945 when the first two were dropped on Hiroshima and Nagasaki in Japan.

It was obvious that the enormous power generated in the explosions could be put to peaceful uses, and the first atomic power-station began production in 1954 at Obinsk, Russia. This power-station, though, operated on only a small scale. The first full-sized atomic power-station began generating electricity on 20th August, 1956, at Calder Hall, Cumberland, at the same time being used to manufacture plutonium – the artificial nuclear fuel.

# Baked Beans

Baked Beans (cooked haricot beans) were first made in 1829 to be eaten with pork. The beans were soaked overnight in earthenware pots. The following morning they were seasoned with mustard, salted pork and molasses and baked in an oven all day. They were ready to eat that night.

Becoming very popular in America, baked beans began to be put into cans at Portland, Maine, USA, in 1875 for the use of fishermen. This was so they could enjoy at sea the same food as they ate on land.

But it was not until 1891 in Indianapolis, USA, that baked beans *in tomato sauce* were first canned by the Van Camp Packing Company.

The American firm of H. J. Heinz started selling canned baked beans in the form described in Britain in 1905, because they thought it might provide a cheap and nourishing food for workmen.

They tried it first in the factory areas in the north of the country, and proved so successful that Heinz opened a factory in Britain in 1928. (*See* CANNED FOOD).

# Ball-bearings

Ball-bearings date from 1543 – except that they were made of wood then. The Italian goldsmith and sculptor, Benvenuto Cellini, had made a statue of Venus and put it on to a wooden plinth. Then he thought it would be a good idea if people could view his latest piece of sculpture from all sides instead of just the front, so half-hidden in the wooden base he inserted four little wooden balls fitted into sockets so that the statue could be turned round 'with the utmost ease'.

He had accidentally discovered how to reduce friction between two moving surfaces, but it took until about 1780 before someone came up with the idea of packing a lot of little balls into a 'ball-race' instead of into separate sockets, and this idea was first used in windmills.

Modern ball-bearings, though, were invented by Philip Vaughan, of Carmarthen, Wales. In 1794 he wanted to find a way of reducing friction in carriage wheels, so made the axles of the carriages which he used in his iron-works run on metal ball-bearings. This made the wheels move more easily and the axles last longer.

But it was not until the bicycle and the motor car were invented, together with machines which could grind the metal balls precisely and accurately, that ball-bearings were able to be used in large quantities.

# Balloon

The two types of balloon, hot-air and gas-filled, were invented in the same year, 1783.

Brothers Joseph and Étienne Montgolfier, paper-makers near Lyons, France, noticed that when their kitchen fire was alight, bits floated up the chimney in the currents of hot air. So they experimented with paper bags. In June, 1782, they made a bag out of cloth lined with paper. It was 33.5 metres (110 ft.) in circumference. In a public square they set this up, lit a fire under-

neath, and the balloon floated off for a mile and a half before landing.

In Paris, a physicist, J. A. C. Charles, heard of what had happened in Lyons, but did not know how it had been done. Hydrogen had only recently been discovered, so in August he sent up a smaller balloon which he filled with hydrogen (by pouring sulphuric acid over iron filings).

Then in September the Montgolfier brothers arrived in Paris with a huge hot-air balloon and sent up some animals in it while the king and queen of France watched. It was on 21st November, 1783 that the first balloon to carry people (two of them) travelled safely for more than 8 kilometres (5 miles) in 25 minutes.

J. A. C. Charles watched with interest, realizing that his was a different type altogether, and on 1st December flew his balloon (very much like a modern gas balloon, even to the valve in the top to allow gas to escape so that it can land), also with two people on board. His balloon flew for 27 miles before landing.

# Ball-point Pen

Ladislao Biro, a Hungarian, was the editor of a magazine. Once when he visited the printing works he noticed how quickly the printers' ink dried, and thought how useful such quick-drying ink would be in a pen.

Escaping from Hungary to Argentina near the beginning of the Second World War, he perfected his pen by 1943, using a tiny ball-bearing instead of a nib to control the flow of the special ink.

A British Government official who happened to be in Argentina at the time, Henry Martin, discovered that the Biro pen worked at any altitude because neither air pressure or changes in the atmosphere affected its performance.

He immediately thought of its use for aircraft navigators. So by 1944 the Biro was being made for the RAF, and Martin began selling them to the general public through his Miles-Martin Pen Company at Christmas, 1945. Within four years ball-points were outselling fountain-pens.

Biro designed his pen to have a cartridge which could be replaced when empty. The first ball-point throw-away design was the Bic introduced into Britain from France in 1958. (*See* FOUNTAIN-PEN).

# Barbed Wire

In 1867 Lucien Smith, of Ohio, USA, designed some barbed wire where the barbs stuck out of blocks of wood strung along a wire, but there was no way of manufacturing it in very long lengths.

Barbed wire more or less as we know it today was invented by a man called Kelly, of the USA, in 1868. It was a twisted wire of two strands with diamond-shaped barbs sticking out from it, and was known as 'Kelly's diamond'.

Farwell Glidden, of New Hampshire, USA, was another who realised that in the American West the enormous cattle ranches had to be fenced in and there was not enough timber to make traditional fences.

His barbed wire appeared in 1873 and, because his mills could produce miles of it, he made a considerable fortune out of his product.

The use of the wire to help keep out an enemy was realised in 1898, when entanglements were used by the American Army in Cuba during the Spanish-American War.

# Barometer

A barometer measures air pressure.

In 1643 an Italian mathematician-physicist, Evangelista Torricelli, experimented with a tube of mercury.

He filled the tube, put his thumb over the open end, then turned the tube upside down in a bowl of mercury. When he took his thumb away, the level of the mercury in the tube fell to leave a 152 millimetre vacuum at the top.

Torricelli suspected that the mercury in the tube was being kept there by the pressure of the air on the mercury in the bowl.

To find if this was so, Blaise Pascal took a similar device up a mountain, and discovered that the higher he climbed, the more the level of the mercury fell. The obvious reason was that the air pressure was getting lower as he climbed higher.

An instrument for measuring air pressure had now been invented. But in 1672 Otto von Guericke noticed that high air pressure generally meant good weather, while low air pressure tended to mean bad weather.

To demonstrate this von Guericke made a tube 10.4 metres (34 ft.) long out of brass, with a closed glass area at the top, filled it with water (in a similar way to which Torricelli had filled his much smaller tube with mercury), with a tub at the bottom, and fastened it to the side of his house where everyone could see it.

A little figure of a man floated on top of the water. He floated high up on good weather, and low down in bad weather – as all his neighbours could see. It didn't amuse them though. They thought he was using witchcraft!

The aneroid barometer (*aneroid* means 'without liquid') uses a similar principle, except that it consists of a vacuum box – the top of which is held by a spring. Changes in air pressure squeeze the box, so moving the spring which is attached to a pointer which moves round a dial.

## Battery

In 1780 an Italian professor of medicine, Luigi Galvani, was at home while his wife was skinning frogs with his scalpel.

The frogs were on a zinc plate. She dropped the scalpel, it landed on a frog's leg, and the leg jerked violently.

After several experiments, Galvani decided that he had found electricity in the frog's muscles, because they always twitched when touched with two different metals at the same time.

However, in 1800 Alessandro Volta, another Italian, decided that Galvani was wrong. He thought that electricity was produced when the metals came into contact – but that the electricity was in the metals themselves, not in the frog's leg.

Volta, after many experiments using different metals, finally invented a stack of copper and zinc discs, with cardboard soaked in salt water to separate them and keep them moist to make a good connection. It worked – the first electric battery had been invented!

In 1801 Napoleon sent for him to demonstrate his remarkable method of producing electricity, because it was realised that the 'Voltaic pile'

13

could be made anywhere, by anybody, so for the first time electricity could be carried about.

You can create an electric shock in your own mouth, often by accident. If a piece of metallic wrapping paper, say from a bar of chocolate, touches a filling in a tooth, you might get a sudden pain.

The reason is that the metal in the filling and the different metal in the paper are giving you an electric shock because the saliva in your mouth is causing a good electrical contact!

# Bicycle

Kirkpatrick Macmillan, a blacksmith in Dumfries, Scotland, invented for himself a wooden frame with a seat, with a wheel at the front of the frame and a slightly larger one at the back, and fitted his wheels with iron tyres. Two pedals moved backwards and forwards and were connected by cranks to the rear wheel.

He invented his bicycle in 1839, but it was only for use by himself, and in 1842 he was fined five shillings (25p) in Glasgow for knocking over a child by riding into him with it.

A coachbuilder of Paris, Pierre Michaux, in 1861, thought of the idea of using a bicycle like Macmillan's but with pedals which went round and round like a handle instead of just backwards and forwards. His son, Ernest, actually put his father's idea to work.

Nine years later the first all-metal bicycle was to appear. Called the Ariel it was made by the Coventry Machine Company – the first machine to have wheels with wire spokes.

A chain driven bicycle was also launched in Coventry in 1880, by the Tangent & Coventry Tricycle Company (later known as Rudge Cycles).

Until this time, the wheels were still of unequal sizes, but John Starley's successful Rover Safety Bicycle appeared in 1885. The wheels were equal in size and there was a geared chain-drive operated by rotating pedals.

In fact, John Starley produced almost the same design as all standard bikes of today. (*See* PNEUMATIC TYRES).

# Braille

Louis Braille invented a system of raised dots on paper in 1829, so that blind people could read printed words.

Each letter of the alphabet had a different sequence of dots, so that by feeling the pattern blind people could identify each letter.

Braille obtained his idea, though, from Captain Barbier, another Frenchman, who in turn developed the ideas of Valentine Hauy who, in 1894, had produced the first book to be printed with raised letters so blind people could feel them.

The Braille system was adopted for use by blind people throughout France in 1854, but in 1932 a style known as Standard English Braille was agreed as the replacement for the original system throughout the world.

# Brassière – *Bra*

Corsets – made out of copper plates – were known to have been worn by women in ancient Crete about 1800 BC. They next became popular in the French and Spanish courts in the 14th century, and certainly throughout Europe and America in the 19th century.

Then in 1902 a 'bust improver' arrived, which was rather similar to the modern bra – woman's undergarment supporting the breasts – and the first 'girdle' in 1912.

The one who really brought about the modern bra, though, was Mary Phelps Jacob, later known as Caresse Crosby. She was a fashionable young woman in New York, USA, and in those days (1914) fashionable women wore heavy corsets of whalebone which were so stiff they could not move about easily.

Just before going to a dance one evening, she and her maid produced a bra out of a couple of handkerchieves, some pink ribbon and some thread, which she wore to the dance.

Her friends were so impressed that they asked her to make them one. Then someone bought a bra from her for one dollar, a designer drew some designs for her (for which he asked 50 dollars but she gave him five dollars instead) – and then nobody was interested any more, until she sold the idea to the Warner Brothers Corset Company, of America, for 15,000 dollars.

Suddenly everyone wanted a bra (well, most women did!) – and if Crosby had been really lucky she would have made not 15,000 dollars out of the idea but *at least* 20,000,000 dollars instead.

## Breakfast Cereal

H. D. Perky, an American lawyer, was in a hotel one day when he watched a man order and consume what seemed to be a very unusual breakfast – whole boiled wheat served with milk.

Henry D. Perky's Shredded Wheat was the outcome – and the very first breakfast cereal, in 1893.

About the same time, Dr John Kellogg and his brother, William, were running a sanitarium (a kind of health farm) in Michigan, USA.

They emphasised healthy eating, and wanted

to provide something other than the ham and baked beans which Americans tended to eat for breakfast at the time.

So, in 1895, Dr Kellogg produced the first flaked breakfast cereal made from wheat. This was named as Granose Flakes.

Three years later, William Kellogg had invented cornflakes, for use in their sanitarium, but they became so popular that after a short while they began producing it for the general public as well.

# Building Society

You might have some money saved in a building society. In a modern building society, people receive interest on the money which they save in it, while those who want to buy property can borrow from a society and repay the money over a number of years.

Interest is charged on the money which is borrowed, and out of the profits the savers' interest is paid.

This is not how the first building societies operated.

The very first was advertised in Birmingham in 1778 by Richard Ketley, although it could have been in existence for two or three years before that date.

In those days, the members of the building society saved enough money between them so that each in turn could buy a house – and whose house was built first was decided by ballot. When every member had his house, the society was closed.

But in 1846 Arthur Strachey, the secretary of the Western Life Assurance and Annuity Society, invented a plan for a *permanent* building society – that is, one in which anyone could invest money and anyone could borrow in order to buy a house, and which did not close down after the houses had been built.

As a result of this idea, 2,000 permanent building societies were founded in the following ten years or so – some of them still existing and among the biggest operating today!

# Bus

The first bus was known as a *carrosse*. It carried eight people, was horse-drawn, and introduced in Paris in 1662 by Blaise Pascal (*see* BAROMETER). Carrosses ran regularly every few minutes whether there were any passengers or not – and that in itself was a great innovation.

By 1823, carrosses were being used in part of the town of Nantes, France, operated by Stanislaus Baudry. Since they were popular, he decided to expand the service, but had to find a name which would let people know that this was a service for all the public – anyone who wanted to ride on them.

The terminus which he used in the centre of Nantes was outside a shop owned by M. Omnes, called *Omnes Omnibus*. The Latin word *omnibus* means 'for everything' – because the shop claimed to sell everything – but it can also mean 'for everybody'.

So omnibus was the word which Baudry gave to his transport service, later reduced just to *bus*.

19

Petrol-driven buses ran between Nantes and Velheuil from 1898. They weighed six tons and carried 18 passengers. The first buses with two decks (double-decker) had appeared long before then, however. These were horse-drawn in London in the year of 1847. Double-decker buses with a totally enclosed upper section appeared in London in 1930, as did the diesel-drawn bus. Horse-drawn buses did not come to a sudden end with the introduction of motor-driven buses either – the last British horse-drawn bus did not come out of service (from Newmarket) until 1932, when one of the horses died!

# Camera

An instrument known as a camera obscura had been in use since the 17th century.

It was a kind of portable drawing instrument with lenses which could be adjusted to make the image of a view appear on a plate of ground glass. Then from that image an artist could paint a picture.

It *might* have been invented by Johann Zahn in 1685, but no one can be absolutely sure.

In 1816 a Frenchman, Joseph Nicéphore Niepce, replaced the ground glass plate on a camera obscura with silver chloride paper, and found – as he had expected one might – he had produced a picture on it. However, he was unable to print a picture from this, because it remained a 'negative' (as in modern photographic negatives, where the dark patches appear light, the light patches dark, and so on).

By 1826, though, using a pewter plate made light-sensitive with asphalt, Niepce produced the first real photograph.

Another Frenchman, Louis Jacques Mande Daguerre, formed a partnership in 1829 with Niepce and in 1839 came the first photograph to be made by the daguerreotype process. (In those ten years they had managed to reduce the length of time for an exposure from eight hours to about 15 minutes!) In the same year the first photographic camera went on sale, made by Alphonse Giroux with Daguerre's signature on every camera.

Meanwhile in Britain, English amateur scientist W. H. Fox Talbot had taken his first photograph in 1835, using a camera made on the same principle as the obscura but with writing paper made light-sensitive with silver chloride instead of the ground glass plates.

His photographs were very small, because his equipment consisted of six-centimetre square wooden boxes which his wife called 'mousetraps'.

Flexible camera film was invented by Alfred Pumphrey, of Birmingham, in 1881. It was sold in packets of 12 and available in several different sizes.

The first roll-film made of celluloid was made by the Eastman Dry Plate Company, of Rochester, New York, USA, to use in their new Kodak camera of 1889.

The foundations of modern photography were then made and little of the basic principle has changed since – except that in 1947 Edwin Land invented the 'instant' Polaroid camera, in which the negative is developed by chemicals released immediately the picture is taken.

# Canned Food

Slight problems over bottling brought about the 'can'. The word 'can' is simply short for 'cannister'.

Nicolas Appert, of Paris, realised that if only the air could be kept out, it would be possible to preserve food for a long time. If food could be preserved in this way, it would be of great use to the French Navy in those days of sailing ships and long voyages from home.

So he bottled broth, meat, beans and peas, and kept the air out with layers of cork which were cut so that the pores in the cork ran horizontally.

His invention was tested in the French Navy in 1804, when it was found that even after three months the food was still fresh.

To solve Appert's problem over air-sealing, in 1812 Bryan Donkin and John Hall, of London, experimented with tin plate cannisters instead of bottles. The cannisters were filled through a small hole in the top, then sealed at once with a disc which was soldered on.

This new idea was taken up by the Royal Navy, having been found to be better than bottles. By 1830, canned food began to appear in British shops.

The idea of attaching a coloured label to state

what a can contained did not come about until one appeared – designed for the firm of Reckhow & Larne, of New York, USA – in the 1860s. (*See* BAKED BEANS).

# Carbon Paper

The quite simple idea for making an exact copy (carbon copy) of what is being written on to a second sheet underneath was invented by Ralph Wedgwood, of London, in 1806.

To make the first carbon paper, he soaked thin paper in ink, then dried it out between sheets of blotting-paper. After that, he placed the paper on which he wanted to write on top.

Placing a sheet of plain paper underneath the carbon paper, the dried ink in between did the rest!

# Carpet-sweeper

Suffering from headaches Melville Bissell, of Michigan, USA, blamed the dust from the straw used to pack crockery in his china shop.

What he needed, he decided, was something which would sweep up the straw without causing dust.

So in 1876 he invented a sweeper with a brush roller. The roller was held in place by springs so that it would move according to the pressure on the handle, brushing all the loose straw and dust into a container.

It was so effective that he and his wife formed the Bissell Carpet Sweeper Company – because they realised that what worked on a floor in a china shop would be a boon in the home.

The Bissell became enormously popular all over the world, and its successors are still in use, despite the later invention of the vacuum cleaner. (*See* VACUUM CLEANER).

# Cash Register

The cash register was invented simply due to the owner of a saloon becoming alarmed at the stealing of money by his barmen, but couldn't find a sure way of stopping them – or even catching them!

James Ritty, of Dayton, Ohio, USA, got the idea of how to solve his problem while he was on board a ship and saw the machine which was used to record the speed of the ship's propellers.

On his return, he at once set about inventing his machine, and put it to use in his saloon.

In 1884, realising that many other saloons and shops had the same problem with some of their employees, after improving his original design, he formed the National Cash Register Company.

The machines went on sale – and his fortune was made.

# Cat's-eye

Percy Shaw, in business as a road repairer in Yorkshire, England, was driving home on a dangerous road in the fog late one night in 1934 and couldn't see easily where he was driving.

Then he saw some reflectors on a poster, and later the eyes of a cat, sitting on a fence, being reflected in his headlights.

He thought it would be an excellent idea if he could bring reflections like those down to ground level and mark where the centre of the road was.

So he invented an ingenious device consisting of a prism and a reflecting mirror, which actually cleaned itself each time a wheel ran over the rubber stud into which it was fitted. The stud was then clipped into a cast-iron base designed to be sunk into the road surface.

To make sure that his idea really worked, he laid the first 50 studs – at his own expense – on a road near Bradford.

Others were thinking on similar lines, and in 1937 the Ministry of Transport tested ten different kinds of reflecting road studs over a five-mile stretch of road. Within two years all of them had broken or worn out except Shaw's Cat's-eyes, which still functioned perfectly.

The Second World War was about to break out, and then an additional usefulness became obvious. When all the street lights in Britain were switched off during the war – the 'blackout' – not only could the Cat's-eyes guide vehicles in the dark, but unlike any other sort of marker Shaw's invention could not reflect light upwards and so draw the attention of enemy aircraft.

# Chewing-gum

Chewing-gum was first made by John Curtis, of
Bangor, Maine, USA, in 1848, on his kitchen
stove. He started production in a factory in Portland, Maine, with a variety of different gums in
1850.

Modern chewing-gum, however, owes its ori-
gins to an American photographer called Thomas
Adams.

He tried experimenting with a tree substance
called chicle as a substitute for rubber in the
production of moulded goods, but the experiments
were not successful.

One day he chewed a lump of chicle and
suddenly thought of adding flavouring and selling
it as gum.

In 1872 he opened a small factory. Business
expanded rapidly, aided by the fact that the Tutti-
Frutti Company began selling it from machines
(the first were erected on platforms of the New
York Elevated Railroad in 1888).

Chewing-gum was introduced to Britain in
1894, but failed to catch on. Then the firm of
Wrigley reintroduced it in 1911, and it probably
became successful for a similar reason as in
America – sweet-shops refused to sell it, so it
appeared on the streets first in vending machines.

# Chocolate

Chocolate – made from cacao seeds – for eating
(as distinct from drinking, which appeared somewhere in the 17th century) had been known in

France and Italy, but the first bars of chocolate were made in a factory set up by Francois-Louis Cailler at Vevey, Switzerland, in 1819.

In 1826 Fry's, of England, were producing 'chocolate lozenges' for medicinal purposes. In 1842 John Cadbury, of Birmingham, started to sell 'French eating chocolate' by the slab. Fry's introduced their chocolate cream stick in 1853.

The first box of chocolates was made by Cadbury's in 1866, and the first milk chocolate was manufactured by Daniel Peter, Cailler's son-in-law, in 1873.

# Christmas Card

Sir Henry Cole decided that he was too busy to write to all of his friends at Christmas, 1853, so he asked John Calcott Horsley, an artist, to design a card for him with a picture on the front.

One thousand were printed, and what Cole did not need were sold by the printer at one shilling (5p) each.

# Cigarette

The cigar (the *cigarro*, derived from the Mayan word *sik'ar*, meaning 'smoking') was introduced to Europe by the Spanish when they returned from their expeditions and conquests in South America.

The cigarette was later invented by beggars in Seville, Spain, who collected cigar-ends from the street, wrapped them in paper and then smoked them!

The first cigarettes to be manufactured were in 1843, in France, made by the state-owned Manufacture Française des Tabacs. These were made by hand.

In Havana, Cuba, a factory to make cigarettes was opened by Louis Susini, still by hand, but in 1853 he installed machinery to roll them.

W. H. Pease, in England, invented machinery to cut and shred the tobacco in 1860.

The first brand-named cigarettes were 'Sweet Threes', produced about 1859 by Robert Gloag in London; the first to be sold in cardboard packets were Wills's 'Three Castles' in 1892; and the first to be sold in a Cellophane wrapping were 'Craven A' in 1931.

# Cinema

It depends on what you call a cinema! The very first film show for the public was given at the Grand Café, Paris, on 28th December, 1895.

The films, made by Louis and Auguste Lumière, were of a train entering a station, a rowing boat in a harbour, and workers coming out of the Lumière factory at Lyons.

The first 'real' permanent cinema was the Vitascope Hall, in New Orleans, USA, opened by William T. Rock in June 1896, but the first 'picture palace' was the Gaumont Palace of Paris, which opened in 1910 and could hold an audience of 5,000 people.

It is possible that the first cinema, in a building

designed just for that purpose, was the Denki-
kan Electric Theatre of Tokyo, Japan, which
opened in 1903.

The first 'talking pictures' did not start with
*The Jazz Singer* in 1929. Films with sound
(on disc) appeared at least as early as in 1902.
(*See* FILM).

# Circus

A former Army sergeant-major, Philip Astley,
was out of work in London in 1769. On
Westminster Bridge he found a diamond ring
which somebody had lost, sold it, and since he
had been in the cavalry, with the money set up
displays of trick horse riding in Lambeth. Money
was made by taking up a collection after each
show.

Within a year he had moved to a better site,
where he charged an admission fee, and employed
a drummer to add to the effect. By 1777 he added
a strong man to the act, and shortly afterwards
two clowns.

The performances were enormously successful.
Altogether Philip Astley helped to found about
19 circuses throughout Europe, and the present
size of the circus ring is exactly that used by
Astley.

# Coffee – *Instant*

Nobody knows who discovered coffee – it could
have been an Ethiopian goatherd called Kaldi,
round about 850 AD, who found his goats getting

very lively after eating the berries off a particular bush.

A coffee extract in the form of a liquid was produced from about 1840, but the first powdered instant coffee was made by Satori Kato, a Japanese chemist living in America, in 1901.

Five years on, an American chemist, G. Washington, produced what he called 'a refined soluble coffee', which was used considerably by the US Army in the First World War.

Modern instant coffee, though, was produced by The Nestlé Company, of Vevey, Switzerland, in 1938 – and they called it Nescafé. The idea of turning coffee beans into a soluble powder had been suggested to them first by the Brazilian Institute of Coffee in 1930 – and it took the firm eight years to get the process right!

# Computer

Charles Babbage, of London, spent from 1823 to 1871 working on his 'analytical machine', designed to take instructions from punched cards, calculate with the aid of a memory bank, and print out a solution.

Unfortunately, despite all his efforts, the very precise engineering work needed to make the machine a complete success was impossible at the time.

Herman Hollerith, of New York, USA, who worked for the US Census Bureau, devised a machine in 1889 which used punched cards to store the information needed for the census, and so halved the time it took to work things out. He left the Census Bureau in 1896 to form the

Tabulated Machine Company to manufacture the
equipment which he had invented – and that
later became part of IBM (International Business
Machines).

The first electronic computer was the Electronic Numerical Integrator and Computer
(known as 'ENIAC'), developed for the US Army
Ordnance in 1946.

Unfortunately, it weighed 30 tons and used
18,000 radio valves! Further, the machine got so
hot while it was working that it could be used
only for short periods of time.

Only after the transistor had been invented
was the modern electronic computer possible, and
the first to be produced was by Remington Rand
in America and Ferranti in Britain, simul-
taneously in 1951. (*See* TRANSISTOR).

# Crossword – *Puzzle*

Arthur Wynne, born in Liverpool, England,
worked in the 'tricks and jokes' department of the
*New York World* newspaper in 1913. He remem-
bered that his grandfather used to play with him
a Victorian game called 'Magic Square', which
involved placing words and letters into spaces.

So for something different for the weekend
supplement of the newspaper on Sunday, 21st
December, 1913, he decided to try something
rather like a magic square. But what he did was
separate the words with black spaces, then added
a list of clues – and the first crossword was
invented.

## ═══════ Dentists' Drill ═══════

A French dentist, Pierre Fauchard, in 1728 invented a hand-drill which he used for loosening decay from his patients' teeth. It was operated by twisting the fingers in opposite directions.

George Washington's dentist, John Greenwood – who also made false teeth for George Washington out of ivory – in 1790 used his mother's spinning wheel to make a drill turn for the same purpose, but the only other person to take up this idea was his son, also a dentist.

Then in 1829 James Nasmyth, of Scotland, inventor of the steam hammer, found a way of using a coiled spring spiral inside a sleeve of metal and thus invented the first flexible cable. Using this idea, in 1858 Charles Merry, of America, devised a dental drill with a flexible cable.

So far, all drills were either hand-operated or operated by a foot pedal, then in 1853 George Harrington, in the Isle of Wight, invented the first power-operated drill. This was a hand-held clockwork machine.

A battery-powered drill was designed by George Green, of Michigan, USA, in 1875. And drills operated from electric power-points came into use in 1908 for the first time.

## ═══════ Diesel Engine ═══════

The engine is named after Dr Rudolf Diesel, of Germany, who produced his first engine in 1893.

In fact it is a compression-ignition engine. The mixture of air and oil inside a cylinder is com-

33

pressed by a piston. This increases the temperature to the point where the oil ignites, the explosion blows the piston back, then the process begins all over again. It does not use petrol but a cheaper, heavier oil, and is a much more efficient engine regarding the use of fuel than a petrol engine.

The first engine of this kind to be manufactured, however, was one invented by Herbert Ackroyd-Stuart in 1890 and made by Hornsby & Sons, of Grantham, Lincolnshire, in 1892. The problem with this one was that in order to start it from cold extra heat had to be supplied to the cylinder head, then removed after the engine was running properly. Hornsby's did produce another version of the Ackroyd engine in 1892 which required no extra heat to start it – and in fact this was actually more like the modern diesel engine than the one which Dr Rudolf Diesel produced a year later.

Diesel, however, continued to develop his engine over the next four years, while Hornsby's developed theirs no further, until he sold the rights in 1897. Diesel committed suicide in 1913, because of his serious financial problems. (*See* PETROL ENGINE).

# Dishwasher

Mrs W. A. Cockran, of Shelbyville, Indiana, USA, took 10 years to perfect her invention, and then made various kinds, including one which needed a steam-engine to drive it.

The Cockran dishwasher first appeared in 1889.

# Diving-bell

Sir Francis Bacon saw a diving-bell in use in 1620, and said it was a sort of metal barrel lowered into the water with the open end downwards.

The modern diving-bell, though, owes much to astronomer and mathematician Sir Edmond Halley (the man who discovered Halley's comet). He made one out of wood which was weighted down with lead, had a glass window, and a bench inside for the people to sit on. It was suspended from a beam attached to a ship. To change the air inside, a tap was opened at the top to let the stale air out when fresh air had been sent down in lead barrels with a leather hose-pipe attached.

Halley even invented a system so that the men could work in the sea outside the diving-bell, wearing a type of headgear with a hose leading back to the fresh air inside the bell – a primitive type of diving-suit.

# Diving-suit

The first closed diving-suit, with a metal helmet screwed on to a breastplate, a rubber collar, watertight cuffs and lead-soled boots, was invented by Augustus Siebe in 1837. He was born in Saxony but lived in England. Air was pumped into the suit from a ship on the surface, and stale air escaped through a valve in the helmet.

The first diving-suit with its own air supply was invented by a French Naval officer, Auguste Denayrouze, in 1872. This had a small barrel on the back to supply compressed air, but still had

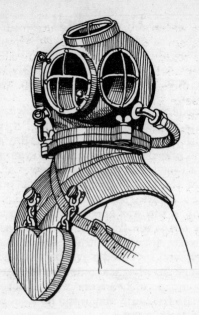

to be attached to the vessel by a line so the diver could return to the surface. (*See* AQUALUNG).

## Duplicating Machine

James Watt (*see* STEAM-ENGINE) needed to keep copies of his business letters, design drawings, and so on. These were written or drawn in ink.

His solution was to wet tracing paper or copying paper with a liquid vinegar, borax and distilled water – pressing the original letter or drawing on to it. The ink passed through, and then he could use the reverse impression which appeared on the tracing or copying paper as a 'master' to run off as many copies as he needed. That was in 1778.

By the year of 1780 he had set up a company to manufacture his latest invention, which was virtually the first offset printing-press as well.

1875 saw US inventor Thomas Alva Edison (*see* ELECTRIC LIGHT *and* GRAMOPHONE) experiment with paper covered in paraffin wax. If someone wrote on waxed paper using a stylus, he reasoned, and then ink was applied, the ink would pass through only where the stylus had cut the wax away.

It worked, but Edison was more interested in using his idea for telegraph tape, so he sold the idea to Albert Dick, a Chicago man who worked in the timber industry, and he produced his first 'mimeograph' in 1887.

The stencil was cut with a stylus, then an inked roller ran over it, so the writing passed through to a blank sheet of paper underneath.

In the meantime (1881), a Hungarian living in London, David Gestetner, produced the first 'real' duplicator and called it the Cyclostyle, and in 1888 produced the first-ever stencil for use with typewriters, as well.

Albert Dick, not to be outdone, produced a mimeograph typewriter stencil two years later.

Competition increased in 1889 when an Austrian, A. D. Kleber, moved to London and invented the first rotary duplicator, where the stencil was attached to a drum and moved round, putting out the the duplicated paper as it went.

His firm changed its name to The Roneo Company in 1908.

George Beidler, working in the Oklahoma land-claim office, could not have heard of duplicating machines.

His office needed many copies of legal documents, and the only thing available in it was constant retyping or copying by hand. So he decided to use a camera and *photograph* the documents, then as many copies as were needed could be printed from the negative . . . so he invented the first photocopier in 1906.

Various improvements followed Beidler's invention, but they all relied on photographic paper, wet chemicals, and either light or heat. Most of them also needed skilled operators. They required something less messy, which was simple and cheap to use.

Chester F. Carlson, a physicist, of New York, after many difficulties, solved the problems in 1938. He called his process xerography (from the Greek word *xēros*, meaning 'dry', and *graphein*, meaning 'to write'). It's a complicated process.

Basically a charge of static electricity was produced on a special photo-conductive plate, then when light was reflected from the material to be copied on to that plate, this changed the pattern of the charge of static electricity.

A powder was sprinkled across which would stick to the pattern of the charge, so reproducing the original, then transferred to ordinary paper and 'fixed' on to it by heat.

Now a simpler method is used, where the copy paper itself forms the special plate and the final copy at the same time.

Surprisingly, nobody in industry was interested. However in 1947 a small family firm, the Haloid Company, decided to risk producing this new invention. And that firm is now known as the Xerox Corporation.

# Dye

How to dye cloth has been known for perhaps thousands of years, but modern synthetic dyes were first produced by English chemist Sir William Henry Perkin.

He was only plain William H. Perkin at the time, 1856, and only 18 years old, working in a shed at the end of his parents' garden in the evenings and at weekends.

He was trying to find a way of making quinine, a drug very effective in the prevention of malaria, out of allyl toluidine, which is a product of coal tar and chemically very like natural quinine.

By adding sulphuric acid and potassium dichromate, all he got was a reddish-brown colour, nothing like quinine at all. So then he tried using aniline instead of allyl toluidine. The aniline was not very pure, and the result was a black sludge.

When Perkin boiled this down with water, to see what came out, the result was purple crystals which he found would dye silk.

Perkin persuaded his father to pay for him to set up a dye factory, and he made so much money out of his aniline dyes that he retired at the age of 35 so that he could spend the rest of his life on chemical research.

He died in 1907, clearly the founder of the modern synthetic dye industry.

# Dynamite

Alfred Bernard Nobel, of Sweden, was the son of Immanuel Nobel, a plywood manufacturer.

At the time, the only explosive which was safe to use was gunpowder. Nitro-glycerine, a yellowish, oily and highly explosive liquid, had been discovered by Ascanio Sobrero in 1846, but it was so likely to explode without warning that it was very dangerous – a severe shake would be enough to set it off. Nobel first invented a detonating cap, using mercury fulminate, which could make nitro-glycerine explode when people wanted it to.

The detonating cap has been the basis of all controlled explosions since.

The trouble was that the nitro-glycerine would still explode when people did *not* want it to! The problem had to be solved, so Nobel tried to soak nitro-glycerine into items such as paper, brick dust, etc, to make it safe to transport. He eventually discovered that a type of dry silica called kieselguhr absorbed nitro-glycerine absolutely safely, only exploding when his detonating cap was used. Dynamite was invented in 1866.

Later, Nobel went on to invent a plastic high explosive in the form of gelignite out of nitro-glycerine and gun cotton. This was even more powerful than dynamite!

Nobel made a huge fortune out of his explosives but, because Sobrero's discovery was the basis of his inventions, he gave him a job for life.

The Nobel prizes, awarded each year to the most outstanding achievements in the areas of world peace, science and literature, are still paid for out of that fortune.

# Elastic

Rubber was first brought to Europe by Charles de la Condamine in 1736 from Peru, where it had been known for centuries. People discovered that it would erase pencil marks, knew it came from somewhere in 'the Indies', so called it *indiarubber*.

Charles Macintosh was a chemist, and Thomas Hancock an inventor, and between them they were experimenting with substances in 1820 to dissolve rubber.

In the process Macintosh put a layer of rubber betweeen two pieces of fabric and came up with the mackintosh – the first waterproof coat! At the same time Hancock invented the first elastic out of strips of rubber glued on to boots and shoes.

Then Hancock heard of a German (whose name he didn't know), who was trying to use threads of rubber to form the lengthwise strands which make a piece of cloth, the 'warp'.

But he was having problems, and asked the firm of Rattier & Guibal, of Paris, to help him out. They couldn't, and in turn asked Hancock to help. He went to Paris, solved the problem, and the first woven elastic was produced by Rattier & Guibal in 1830.

Elastic-sided boots were invented, using this elastic cloth, by James Dowie in 1837, and the first 'knicker elastic' made out of a flat elastic braid appeared in Britain in 1887.

The problem with ordinary rubber is that it can become sticky in hot weather, and lose its elasticity if the weather is cold.

In America, Charles Goodyear was trying to improve rubber. By sheer accident, he overheated

41

a mixture which he had made out of rubber, sulphur and white lead (lead carbonate, used in paints) – and found he had produced a rubber which didn't burn easily or melt – vulcanized rubber, in fact.

He tried to sell the idea to Charles Macintosh in England, but by that time Thomas Hancock, who was still working with Macintosh, had already worked out for himself what Goodyear had done.

So in 1844, the same material came out in America and England within a few days of each other. Two years later Alexander Parkes (*see* PLASTIC) found that rubber could also be vulcanized by dipping it into a solution of sulphur monochloride (now known as disulphur dichloride), and this was the best way of making rubber for balloons, teats for babies' bottles, and such like.

In the meantime (1845), Stephen Perry, of London, realised what else could be done with elasticated rubber. He started to make the first rubber bands, 'for papers, letters, etc.'

## Electricity

The genius of electricity was English chemist Sir Michael Faraday, born in London in 1791, for without him there would have been no modern uses of electricity.

Oddly, he made the first electric motor before he found how to generate electricity, so when he invented this he could use only a battery to operate it.

In 1820, Professor Hans Christian Oersted, of Denmark, had noticed that when a magnetic needle was suspended near a wire carrying an electric current, the needle would move either towards or away from it.

Faraday decided that there must be a connection between electricity and magnetism, and after several experiments in 1821 he suspended a length of copper wire from a hook so that its lower end touched a dish of mercury. When he passed a current from a battery through the hook the wire moved round and round until he switched the battery off.

This first, primitive motor was of no practical use, because it couldn't drive anything – but it did prove that magnetism and electricity were closely connected.


## DYNAMO

Ten years later, in October 1831, Faraday managed to produce electricity without using a battery. He had a coil of wire wrapped round a cylinder, and a bar magnet which he moved in and out of the coil by hand. Electricity was produced!

So he improved his discovery by setting up a copper disc on a spindle between two powerful magnets, fitted a handle to the end of the spindle and turned it. The result – a continuous supply of electricity.

So with these two machines Faraday had invented both *alternating current* (where the current changes direction each time the magnet moves) and *direct current* (where the electricity is produced of the same kind as that made by using a battery).

43

## TRANSFORMER

This is a way of either increasing or reducing the voltage of the electricity supply. Faraday invented this, too, in 1831.

He found that if he passed a current into a coil of wire, and then interrupted that current, electricity would be produced in another coil wrapped around the first.

What was more, how much the voltage could be increased or reduced depended on the amount of turns of wire he had in each of the two coils. So when he used an alternating current, he could make the voltage as big or as little as he wished.

The electricity carried in the power lines on pylons is 33,000 volts – and very dangerous. Using a transformer, this is reduced to a much safer 240 volts for use in people's homes.

In some countries, the voltage is reduced to 110 volts by the same process. Also a transformer is what is used to reduce the normal voltage to a much lower one – usually 12 volts when you plug in, for example, an electric train set.

# ══ Electric Blanket ══

An American, named S. I. Russell, invented an electric heating pad in 1912 to warm patients suffering from tuberculosis (wasting disease affecting various parts of the body) who had to sleep out of doors.

In 1926 the British Ex-Services Mental Welfare Society started manufacturing a heated pad invented in Germany, which later became the Thermega underblanket. In America 1937 saw the idea of a heated *over*-blanket become popular, with the aim of heating the bed rather than just the person sleeping in it, while the idea of an electric *under*-blanket became popular in Britain at about the same time.

## Electric Fan

The electric fan was invented by Schuyler Skaats Wheeler, chief engineer of the Crocker & Curtis Electric Motor Company, of New York, in 1882.

## Electric Light

The very first electric light was invented by James Lindsay, of Scotland, in 1835. He was a schoolmaster.

It operated from a battery, and he did not develop it further but kept it only for his own use. All that is known about it is that it worked, and involved using a glass tube with the air sucked out to create a vacuum.

Both Sir Joseph Swan, of Newcastle-upon-Tyne and Thomas Alva Edison, of New Jersey, USA, invented the modern electric lamp quite independently of each other in the same year, 1878.

Present-day electric lamps use a metal filament to glow white-hot and so give light, but both Swan and Edison used a filament made of carbon. The first successful Edison lamp did not appear, though, until October 1879, when it burned for 13½ hours before failing.

In 1880, Edison changed to carbonised paper filaments and began manufacturing his lamps for use by the public. In the meantime, Swan had changed to a carbonised cotton thread filament and produced these for the public in November, of the same year.

Then both Swan and Edison began suing each other in the lawcourts for stealing each other's inventions. Eventually, however, they joined forces and worked together, because it appeared neither had actually stolen anything from the other.

## Electric Motor

Chemist Michael Faraday's original motor had no practical use (*see* page 42). The first motor which was capable of driving equipment was invented by Thomas Davenport, of Rutland, Vermont, USA, in 1837.

## Electric Razor

A retired American Army officer, Lieutenant-Colonel Jacob Schick, invented the electric razor in 1928. It started to be manufactured in 1931. (*See* SAFETY RAZOR).

## Electric Torch

The first electric torch was made by the Bristol Electric Lamp Company in 1891, and it weighed two pounds – including the battery. It was rather like the old-fashioned bull's-eye lantern in shape.

The first cylinder-shaped torches were made by the American Electric & Novelty Manufacturing Company, of New York, in 1898. Later the firm changed its name to the American Ever-Ready Company.

The Ever-Ready electric torch first began to be sold in Britain in the year 1900.

## Elevator – *Lift*

The first elevator was installed in King Louis XV of France's private apartment at the Palace of Versailles in 1743.

The next one known was fitted into the Coliseum at Regent's Park, London, by Decimus Burton in 1829. It was enlarged to carry 10 to 12 people by 1848, and ceased to exist when the building was destroyed by fire in 1875.

The inventor of the modern lift or elevator, though, was Elisha Otis, who first showed his invention at the Crystal Palace Exposition, New York, in 1853. It attracted enormous attention because of the way in which he demonstrated it.

He was carried up in the elevator each day, then each time ordered the wires which held it to be cut. The elevator remained exactly where it was because of the safety device built into the mechanism.

Until then, elevators were very slow, because to make them move quickly would be far too dangerous. The Otis elevator made high-speed passenger lifts safe even in the tallest buildings.

Otis lifts were first installed in departmental

47

stores (Haughwort & Company, New York, in 1857), hotels (Fifth Avenue Hotel, New York, 1859), and office buildings (Equitable Life Assurance Society Building, New York, in 1868).

# Escalator

A 'moving staircase' was invented by Jesse Reno, of New York, USA, in 1892, and it was first used on a pier at Coney Island, an American amusement park, in 1896.

It was a conveyor belt made up of wooden slats and driven by an electric motor. It was called the Reno Inclined Elevator.

Another American, Charles Wheeler, in the same year also invented an escalator. His had flat steps, like modern ones.

This was improved in its design by Charles Seeberger in 1898 (because the original Wheeler escalator was never actually built), and the Otis Elevator Company at once saw its potential use and began manufacturing it from 1899 onwards.

# ≡ Film – *Moving Pictures* ≡

The motion picture only became possible in its present form when celluloid film, in rolls, was made by George Eastman of the Kodak Company, USA.

Various people had tried making motion pictures before, notably Louis Le Prince, a Frenchman living in America, and William Friese-Green in England, but Thomas Alva Edison put an assistant to work with the Eastman film to produce moving pictures – and the invention was ready for use by 1891.

It was called the Kinetoscope, and was designed for just one person to view the pictures at a time.

The real inventors of the modern movies, however, were Auguste and Louis Lumière, of France, because the main problem was the film projector.

When you see a film, what you are actually seeing is an enormous number of separate photographs. Each remains still for either one-sixteenth (for silent films) or one-twenty-fourth (for sound films) of a second before it moves on and the next one takes its place.

Because of what is known as 'persistence of vision' in your eye, you seem to see the pictures actually moving.

But stopping and starting the film so often would break the material of which it is made. The Lumière brothers finally solved the problem after watching how a sewing-machine worked, and then using a somewhat similar type of claw movement to that which moves the cloth under the needle. So they managed to keep the film moving while actually stopping it many times per second in front of the lens. The film is kept slack above and below the claw mechanism by means of a loop.

The first 'modern' movie ever was demonstrated by the Lumière brothers in 1895. (*See* CINEMA).

═══════ # Fire Extinguisher ═══════

A German doctor called Fuches thought it would be a good idea to fill glass balls with salt solution, in 1734. He made some for putting out fires, but they were not successful – mainly because you were supposed to throw them at the fire!.

The modern extinguisher was invented by Captain George Manby in 1816, after he had seen a disastrous fire.

It was a metal cylinder filled three-quarters full with water, and the remaining quarter of the space filled with compressed air. Then when the valve was opened the air forced the water out through a hose.

Very few were sold, just a few hundred, and it was not until the end of the 19th century that someone thought of the idea of using carbon dioxide gas instead of compressed air.

Pushing a plunger broke a glass bottle of acid which spilled on to sodium carbonate (washing soda) and so produced the gas inside the extinguisher when it was needed.

During the Second World War, this was improved to contain the carbon dioxide under pressure in a cartridge – but the 'soda-acid' extinguisher can still be found in use to this day.

# ═══ Fluorescent Light ═══

In 1895 Antoine-Henri Becquerel, of France, passed electricity through a glass tube which was empty apart from a rarefied gas, and it glowed.

To make this glow brighter he coated the inside of the glass tube with a fluorescent powder – a chemical which absorbs light in one colour and in its place gives out light in another.

From this sort of experiment came the neon light.

However, the first fluorescent light giving out the sort of colour which could be used in homes, offices, shops and factories was invented by Arthur H. Compton of the General Electric Company, of America. He demonstrated it properly for the first time in 1936, at a dinner held in Washington, USA.

The GEC and the Westinghouse Corporation both commenced making fluorescent lamps in 1939 for sale to the general public – but in Britain, probably because of the Second World War, they did not come into general use until October 1945.

The greatest advantage of these lights is that they use very low voltages, are much cheaper to run than ordinary light bulbs (because they use less electricity), last longer, don't get hot, and they can be made to give out many different shades of colour. (*See* NEON LIGHT).

# Fountain-pen

Several attempts to make a pen which contained its own ink supply were made from as early as 1656.

Samuel Pepys, who wrote the famous diary, had one in 1663.

The way this worked was by filling a tube above the (quill) nib with ink, then pressing a plunger to keep the ink flowing.

Joseph Bramah improved this in 1809 by using a barrel which could be squeezed instead of a plunger which had to be pressed, then the only improvement after that for many years was the invention of the rubber ink-sac by Walter Mosely in 1859.

There were problems with these pens, of course – as an American insurance salesman, Lewis Edson Waterman, discovered.

He was using a fountain-pen to write out an insurance policy for a client, the ink ran out all over the policy, and he lost the sale. So he set out to make a fountain-pen which would work properly all the time.

In 1884 he produced the first practical fountain-pen. It was different from modern ones in that it had to be filled with an eye-dropper, instead of sucking up the ink straight from the bottle.

# Frozen Food

Clarence Birdseye was in Labrador during the years 1912 to 1915, as part of a United States Government survey of the fish and wildlife there.

He noticed that when the local people caught fish in very low temperatures, the fish froze stiff as soon as they were taken out of the water.

He thought it might be possible to keep vegetables fresh in a similar way, so he put some into a tub of water and let them freeze solid. It worked!

Back in America, in 1924 he set up his own company in New Jersey to freeze food. It was so successful that in 1929 he sold it to the Postum Company for 22,000,000 dollars! The condition was that they kept his name on the label as Birds Eye.

The first vegetables, fish and meat in individual packs went on sale in 1930, sold from ice-cream refrigerators in the shops.

The first frozen foods which were cooked before freezing, so that they only needed heating up at home, were introduced by Birds Eye in 1939.

Because of the observation and invention of Birdseye, therefore, all modern frozen foods, home freezers, etc, were able to develop.

# Gas Fire

Philippe Lebon, of Bruchey, France, invented the very first gas fire in 1799. It both heated and provided light for a room, but it was not successful because people objected to its unpleasant smell.

Robert von Bunsen, however, invented his Bunsen burner in 1855 in Germany, for use in laboratories. Air is drawn in with the gas and as a result there is a much hotter flame.

In the same year the firm of Pettit & Smith in England made use of Bunsen's invention to produce the first practical gas fire for sale to the general public – and Bunsen's is still the main principle behind the modern gas fire.

# Gas Mask

Poison gas as a weapon of war was *not* outlawed at The Hague International Peace Conference in 1899, so in 1915, in the First World War, the German Army decided to use gas against the British and French troops.

To overcome this, the British and French were provided with chemically-treated pads to tie over their noses and mouths.

These were developed very soon into a respirator with a mask which fitted tightly round the face with a tube leading to a container filled with charcoal, through which the poison gases were filtered.

In the Second World War, the entire population of Britain were supplied with gas masks, as well as the Army, just in case gas was used again.

The Army type had the filter carried at the side, but the civilian type fitted over the face, was held on by straps round the head, and had the filter fitted into the mask just under the chin. All types had a clear panel at the front so that the wearer could see.

Modern gas masks are used in mines and chemical plants, and by firemen, rescue teams, and so on.

# Gas Stove

James Sharp, of the Northampton Gas Company, England, invented the gas stove for use in his own kitchen.

The first one was used in 1834 at the Bath Hotel, Leamington Spa.

In 1836 he opened a factory in Northampton to manufacture gas stoves – and made use of the Bunsen principle from about 1855.

# Geiger Counter

This device, for detecting radioactive material, was invented by Hans (Johann) Wilhelm Geiger in 1910. He was a German nuclear physicist working at Manchester University.

It was originally developed in 1908 for counting the part of radiation known as alpha particles.

Nowadays the Geiger either makes clicking noises which sound faster as more radiation is found, or reads off the amount of radiation on a dial.

There are three types of radiation – alpha, beta and gamma particles. Modern Geiger counters can distinguish between the three kinds and can also indicate what sort of radiation is present.

# ≡ Gramophone – *Record-player* ≡

First, Thomas Alva Edison invented the phonograph. The telephone (*see* TELEPHONE) had just been invented.

Edison realized that since it worked because of the vibrations in the diaphragm of the telephone mouthpiece when somebody talked into it, if some kind of stylus could be attached, then it could produce a pattern on something soft, so the sound could be recorded permanently. It should then be possible to play it back, using a similar stylus, and so reproduce the original sound.

His first phonograph used a cylinder of tin foil. A stylus, moved along it by a screw while the cylinder was turning, cut a sound into the tin foil from a microphone. To make it play back, a hearing-tube with a stylus attached was used instead of the microphone.

That was in 1877, when Edison himself recited the nursery rhyme, 'Mary had a little lamb', into his machine.

Over the next few years he improved his invention, eventually using waxed cylinders instead of tin foil.

The phonograph cut grooves as the stylus moved up and down.

The modern disc, where the stylus moves from side to side instead, was invented by Emile

Berliner and was first demonstrated in Philadelphia, USA, in 1888. The first discs were made of vulcanized rubber.

Records made of shellac came into being in 1897, the same year as the first disc recording studio was opened by the Berliner Gramophone Company.

By 1898 the Gramophone Company had opened in Britain, and a factory which they owned opened in Hanover, Germany, to mass produce seven-inch records.

Paper labels appeared on records in 1900 – the famous 'His Master's Voice' picture was the first (now known as HMV).

The Decca Company manufactured the first portable (wind-up) gramophone in 1913, and the first disc to be recorded electrically instead of mechanically appeared in 1920. Electric gramophones or record-players came in 1925.

The first long-playing records (LPs) actually appeared in 1904, but those playing at 33⅓ revolutions per minute, as now, were not produced until 1931.

Discs made of shellac broke easily, but these began to be replaced by discs made of almost unbreakable vinylite in 1946.

That led the way to LPs as we know them today, when Peter Goldmark developed the first 'microgroove' disc in 1948, with full production starting a year later. This marked the end of the old '78s' – records playing at 78 revolutions per minute.

# Hearing-aid

In Victorian days, deaf people who could afford a hearing-aid used a 'speaking trumpet'.

They put the narrow end into their ear and pointed the trumpet at whoever was speaking. Queen Victoria herself had one, made of silver.

Then Alexander Graham Bell, a Scot who specialised in working for the deaf, invented the telephone, and electric hearing-aids became possible. (*See* TELEPHONE).

The first electric hearing-aid was invented by Miller Reese Hutchinson, of New York, in 1901. It was about the size of a large portable radio, with a receiver like that of a telephone to hold to the ear. Hutchinson also invented the Klaxon horn, used on early motor cars, and the joke went around that he had invented it only to send people deaf, so they would have to buy one of his hearing-aids.

It took until 1935 before a hearing-aid was invented by A. Edward Stevens which was small. This weighed just over a kilogram (2½ lb.) and was sold under the name of Amplivox. It was not until the invention of the transistor (*see* TRANSISTOR) that hearing-aids could be made very tiny, and the first transistorized hearing-aid, the Sonotone, began to be produced in America in 1952.

# Helicopter

Helicopters, to use as toys, were known as far back as the 14th century.

Rotor blades, like those on a windmill, but horizontal instead of vertical, were fitted into a holder on a spindle, then made to move round fast by wrapping string around and pulling. The toy would then rise into the air.

The first helicopter which could carry a human being was designed by E. R. Mumford in 1905.

It had six propellers, a petrol engine and was built by William Denny & Brothers, of Dumbarton, Scotland.

By 1912 it had managed flights of up to just over three metres (10 ft.) from the ground – but had to be tethered so that it would not fly away.

Paul Cornu, of France, invented a practical helicopter in 1907. It did not fly very high, or for long, but was not attached to the ground.

It took until 1924 before Étienne Oehmichen produced a machine capable of flying forwards as well as upwards – and the first 'real' helicopter was invented.

In the meantime, Spaniard Juan de la Cierva had invented the Autogiro in 1923. This was different from a helicopter because the rotor blades had no motor to drive them – the rotors acted as revolving wings, and the machine was pulled forward by a propeller.

Then in 1936 Louis Breguet and René Dorand, of France, devised a helicopter capable of flying at 67 miles an hour at a height of 157½ metres (517 ft.).

In Germany, in 1936, Dr Heinrich Focke produced a much more advanced design, the Focke-Wolfe FW61, which could fly at 76 miles an hour and at a height of more than 2,400 metres (nearly 8,000 feet).

Finally, with the Sikorsky VS-300, used by the US Army from 1942, the modern helicopter had arrived.

# Hotel

Hotels are a more modern idea than most people realize.

Before 1774, inns and taverns were mainly for the provision of drink and food rather than for putting up travellers, but in this year David Low opened Low's Grand Hotel at Covent Garden, London.

He called it 'a public place of residence designed primarily for the accommodation of families'. This was the first hotel anywhere in the world.

Low gave up his hotel in 1780 because he could not make it profitable, but it was taken over by others, and run as an hotel, until the late 19th century.

In the meantime, many other hotels appeared all over the world, including Tremont House, Boston, Massachusetts, USA, which in 1829 was the first hotel to be equipped with bathrooms – eight of them for 250 guests.

# Hovercraft

In 1955 Christopher Cockerell, an English boat-designer (later knighted) had some empty tin cans and got an idea.

Using a vacuum cleaner to blow instead of suck, he found he could make the cans lift off his kitchen table due to the cushion of air which formed underneath. He experimented further.

In 1959 the first full-size hovercraft was made by the firm of Saunders-Roe in the Isle of Wight, based on Cockerell's design. In the same year the

hovercraft was developed to the stage where the first craft crossed the English Channel. 1962 saw the first regular passenger service between Cheshire and Wales, and in 1968 a cross-Channel service.

# Hydrofoil

A hydrofoil acts like a boat until it picks up speed, then it skims over the water on legs. In that way it overcomes the resistance of the water and so can go much faster than a traditional-style boat.

Enrico Forlamini, an Italian, built a small hydrofoil in 1905.

Alexander Graham Bell (*see* TELEPHONE) saw it in action and as a result decided to design his own, using Forlamini's ideas. That one achieved a water-speed record of 71 miles an hour in 1918.

Both German and British inventors, including Christopher Hook, improved the design in the following years, but it was not until the 'Supramar' hydrofoils began production in Italy in the 1950s that the modern hydrofoil became a really practical alternative to boats – on water which would not get too rough!

Since then, both Russia and America have produced their own designs.

# Ice-cream

Fruit juices kept cold by being packed around with snow were known to the Pharaohs of ancient Egypt – but these were 'water-ices' rather than proper ice-cream.

Something like ice-cream is known to have been served to King James II of England in 1686 at the price of £1 per portion, while in 1660 his elder brother, Charles II, is known to have eaten ice-cream in Paris while he was in exile.

It is also known that George Washington, the President of the USA, was keen on ice-cream in 1790.

Probably the ice-cream of that time was based on the discovery of Blasius Villefranca, living in Rome, who in 1550 found that freezing-point could be reached if saltpetre or salt were added to snow, and so managed to produce a creamy, frozen mixture.

Then in 1851 Jacob Fussell, a milk supplier of Baltimore, USA, found that cream was going to waste at certain times of the year.

He set himself up as a supplier of ice-cream to other milkmen, so establishing the world's first ice-cream factory.

Such a factory was set up in London in 1870 for the benefit of a large number of Italian immigrants who had arrived about that time, who through selling ice-cream became known as 'hokey-pokey' men, so called because they used to shout in Italian 'Ecco un poco', which means 'Here's a bit'.

The ice-cream cornet was invented by accident in 1904, when in Louisiana, USA, the girl-friend of an ice-cream salesman rolled a wafer biscuit around her ice-cream to stop it dripping on to her clothes – so the story goes.

On the other hand, it is more likely that it was invented by an Italian immigrant to the USA, Italo Marcioni, in 1903.

Ice-cream really became popular in 1922, when Thomas Wall, a British sausage manufacturer in Acton, was worried about short-time working in his factory during the summer months, when fewer sausages were being purchased.

So he began to manufacture the first wrapped blocks of ice-cream as an alternative, selling them cheaply. It was an instant success. This was somewhat curious as shops refused to sell his ice-cream blocks, at least at first.

Because of this, Wall sold them on the streets instead, directly to the customers, from tricycles with 'Stop me and buy one' on the front – hailing the beginning of ice-cream vans as well.

## Insulin

If you suffer from diabetes, the body is not able to control the sugar in it because of the lack of a hormone in a part of the body called the pancreas.

Until the discovery of how to make that missing hormone, if you had diabetes you were almost certain to die.

In 1921 Dr Frederick Grant Banting and Charles Best found how to produce that hormone, which was later called insulin.

The first patient to be treated with it was in Toronto, Canada, where Banting worked in January 1922. He was a 14-year-old boy called Leonard Thompson.

# Jeans

It is likely that the original closely-woven material was called jean.

Levi Strauss from Bavaria, now an immigrant into the USA, took some bales of this cloth to San Francisco at the time of the Gold-Rush.

He intended to earn a living by using it to make tents and coverings for wagons. He found, though, that too many others had already arrived before him, in 1850, all with the same idea.

A gold-miner complained to him that ordinary trousers wore out too quickly when he was working, so Strauss began to make trousers out of this tough material instead. These trousers did not fray or tatter easily, and soon became very popular.

A gold prospector then took his Levi Strauss 'jeans' to a blacksmith to have some rivets added because without them the pockets weren't strong enough to carry his rock specimens in!

The idea was patented in May 1873 and continues today, an example being Levi Strauss & Co's Original Riveted 501 range, with button fly.

# Jet Engine

The first turbo-jet engine to fly was fitted to a Heinkel He-178 in 1939, designed by Hans von Ohain.

At the same time, young RAF officer Frank Whittle in Britain was working on the same idea – his designs, in fact, came out before von

Ohain's, but the first aircraft to use a Whittle engine did not fly until 1941.

The original idea for 'reaction propulsion' probably came from Joseph Montgolfier (*see* BALLOON) in 1783. He thought that the hot air from his balloon could be made to shoot out backwards from the balloon and so drive the balloon forwards, but the Montgolfier brothers were unable to make the idea work.

The German Luftwaffe still had the only really successful jet engines (especially on the Messerschmitt Me-262 fighter plane) by the end of the Second World War. Then the Whittle engines took over, and all subsequent jet engine designs basically owe their existence to Frank Whittle.

# Laser

A laser beam is an extremely intense narrow parallel beam of light. The word itself is derived from the words 'light amplification by stimulated emission of radiation'.

Albert Einstein said in 1917 that it should be possible to make rays of light of the correct frequency be directed on an atom to make it release its energy in the form of light, but it was not until 1958 that the right calculations were made by A. L. Schawlow and C. H. Townes to make this possible.

Schawlow and Townes's first experiments failed, but by 1960 they had succeeded in generating the first laser beam, using a type of ruby.

Since then, the laser has been used in high-powered versions for cutting through metal, in delicate surgery such as in eye operations – and for putting on special effects at pop concerts and for street Christmas light displays!

# Lawn-mower

The first attempt, using a pair of carriage wheels to move a large circular blade near to the ground, appeared in 1805, designed by Thomas Plucknett.

The modern lawn-mower, though, was invented by Edward Budding, of Stroud, Gloucestershire, in 1830, designed for 'cropping or shearing the vegetable surface of lawns, grass-plots and pleasure grounds'.

It was a 19-inch roller mower, looking very similar to modern machines except that the box to collect the cut grass looked like a seed-tray (because it originally was!).

Budding worked in a textile factory, and got the idea from a machine which sheared the rough surface from the cloth. His first machines were made by the Phoenix Iron Works, near Stroud.

Then in 1832 the firm of Ransome, Sims & Jefferies, of Ipswich, started to manufacture them. Side wheels were introduced in 1869, and the same firm produced the first motor mower in 1902. It worked, and was designed by James Ransome.

The first electric mower was then introduced in 1926. The hover mower, of course, had to wait until the idea of the hovercraft had been developed in the early 1960s.

# Lightning Conductor

In 1749 the Academy of Bordeaux, France, offered a prize for anyone who could show that there was some connection between electricity and thunder.

In America, although not a competitor, Benjamin Franklin and some friends erected sharpened pieces of metal and found that they attracted electricity during a thunderstorm.

Then in 1752 he flew a kite into a cloud during a thunderstorm, with a metal key attached, and got an electric shock. He decided that lightning, not thunder, was composed of electricity.

With this in mind he fastened a steel-pointed iron rod to the side of his house, making it project well above the roof, placing the end of it well into the ground.

His reasoning was that if anything was going to be struck by lightning it might as well be this rod rather than his house! In addition he arranged for similar lightning conductors to be attached to the State House and the Academy Building in Philadelphia to protect them from lightning.

The idea caught on. In the meantime, however, some clergymen objected to their use because, they said, lightning was the wrath of God.

A French scientist came to the conclusion that such conductors would attract the lightning and so cause damage to the buildings instead of saving them from it. Again in France, one man was even tried for blasphemy for daring to tempt God by putting up a lightning conductor!

The first public building in Britain to be protected by a lightning conductor was St Paul's Cathedral in 1770 – a year after one had been fitted to St Jacob's Church in Hamburg, Germany.

# Lock and Key

The lock and key was a Chinese invention, dating from at least four thousand years ago. It was changed and improved over the centuries, but the modern lock and key started with one invented by Joseph Bramah in 1778. (*See* WATER-CLOSET).

He used six sliding metal plates with notches cut into them, which had to be moved by the key into one particular position before the lock could open.

In 1818 came the Chubb lock, invented by Charles Chubb, an ironmonger who later went on to make fireproof safes. This had an extra lever inside which fixed the bolt if anyone tried to 'pick' the lock instead of using the correct key.

Locks for people's front doors are often Yale locks. These were invented by an American, Linus Yale, in 1851. He changed the shape to a cylinder and used a flat key which had to fit exactly into the notches in the various tumblers inside.

Two brilliant ideas: first, the lock fits right through the door instead of being attached just to one side of the wood, and even more important, the notches in the tumblers can be cut into so many different shapes that it is almost impossible to find two Yale locks which are exactly the same, so you have to possess the correct key for your particular lock, otherwise it will not open.

## Logarithm

If one number is expressed as the power of another number, that power is the logarithm.

That is, if $9=3^2$ (i.e. $9=3\times3$), then the power, 2, is the logarithm.

This may seem complicated, but it means that by using logarithms multiplication, division, etc, become a lot quicker and easier.

John Napier, of Merchiston, Scotland, after twenty years of working this out, produced the first book of logarithmic tables in 1614.

Henry Briggs, professor of geometry at Gresham College, London, realised that this new invention would help enormously in calculations involving navigation and surveying, many of which were very complicated.

71

In its day, the invention of logarithms was as important as the invention of the computer centuries later. Napier and Briggs worked out more logarithms until Napier died in 1617 and Briggs in 1624.

It was Adrian Vlacq who completed the tables in 1628.

# Machine-gun

A gun with many barrels first appeared in 1339, the *ribauld*. Each touch-hole was lit in turn, so that the barrels fired one after the other. By 1387 one version of the ribauld had 144 barrels – but the problem of the time it took to reload the gun after all the barrels had been fired remained. It was not a success.

James Puckle invented a gun in 1718 with six cylinders each with six chambers. The peculiar thing about it was that it was designed to fire round bullets at Christians and square-shaped ones at Moslems.

The Gatling gun, which appeared during the American Civil War, had 10 barrels with bullets fed into them from a drum. Each barrel fired in turn to produce a firing rate of 350 bullets a minute. A handle was turned to make it operate. This tended to jam rather easily.

Hiram Maxim was an American who later became a naturalised Englishman. In 1881 he was told by another American that if he wanted to make a lot of money, all he had to do was invent something that would allow Europeans to kill each other more easily!

Heeding that advice, by 1883 he had invented a gun in which each time a shot was fired the recoil not only expelled the used cartridge but brought in the next cartridge to take its place.

He fitted the bullets to a belt. The gun would continue to fire automatically until the belt was used up – all you had to do was press the trigger. Since it became hot while in use he designed it to be water-cooled.

The Maxim machine-gun was first used in the

war between Russia and Japan, and in the First World War it was used by both sides – and made his fortune.

====== Man-made Fibre ======

Sir Joseph Swan, one of the two inventors of the electric light, was trying to find a better filament for his lamps (*see* ELECTRIC LIGHT).

He squirted nitro-cellulose through a tiny hole into a liquid which would make it form a thickened mass (a coagulating fluid) in 1885, and what came out was a thread fine enough to be made into fabrics.

In France, Count Hilaire de Chardonnet was dealing with the problem of diseases in silkworms in the same year. To find an alternative to silk he tried a similar experiment.

He called his product rayon, and started producing it at Besançon in 1892. Unfortunately, it was not satisfactory for woven cloth. It was, however, for making braids, fringes and so on.

Meanwhile, back in Britain C. S. Cross had invented viscose in 1892 by treating wood-pulp with, among other things, caustic soda (sodium hydroxide).

Together, he and C. H. Stearn produced viscose rayon which could be both woven and dyed, at Kew, Surrey, in 1898. The firm of Courtauld started production at Coventry (1905) – using the Cross and Stearn process and opened factories in Germany and France.

In 1938 Dr Wallace Carothers in America discovered nylon, which was then manufactured by the Du Pont Company in the USA. Being the first synthetic yarn the importance of nylon was due to its being entirely made out of the chemicals benzene, nitrogen, oxygen and hydrogen.

Terylene, made from petroleum, was discovered in 1941 – and since then have followed other 'chemical' fibres and material, such as acrylic fibres, and polyvinyl chloride (commonly known as PVC, rather like a plastic leather). (*See* PLASTIC).

# ===== Margarine =====

Napoleon III of France organised a competition to find something to replace butter in the French Navy and for use by the 'less prosperous classes'.

Hippolyte Mège-Mouriez decided that whatever a cow could do naturally, somebody ought to be able to do artificially, so set about finding a way of doing it.

In 1869 he came up with a compound of suet, skimmed milk, pig's stomach, cow's udder and bicarbonate of soda.

Since part-way through the manufacturing process it looked like a string of pearls, he called it margarine, from the Greek word *margarites*, meaning 'a pearl'.

He thought he was going to make his fortune, and set up a factory to make this new product, but the Franco-Prussian War broke out almost at once and the factory had to close.

But two brothers, Jan and Henri Jurgens, who were butter merchants in Oss, Holland, bought the process from him, opened a factory in 1871, and started production.

Soon they and a rival firm of butter merchants

at Oss, the Van den Burghs, were making large amounts of margarine, and it sold well in Holland and England – but not in America, because it looked rather like cooking fat.

A shortage of animal fats made the two firms begin to experiment with vegetable oils instead. This became successful in 1910 when a method which hardens fats by adding hydrogen was discovered.

Later, when vitamins A & D were added and the margarine began to look like butter, the Americans started to eat it as well. By this time, the two firms had joined forces to become known as Van den Burgh & Jurgens.

# Match

John Walker was a chemist of Stockton-on-Tees, England, and he invented the first match by accident in 1826.

He had been using a stick to stir a mixture of potash (potassium carbonate) and antimony. When he scraped it against the stone floor to get rid of the blob which had formed on the end of the stick, it promptly burst into flames.

The days of the tinder-box were now over! Within a year matches were being sold in boxes of 100, and were first made out of strips of cardboard. Since these bent too easily Walker soon changed this idea for flat wooden splints of wood.

The safety match was invented by Johan Lundstrom, of Sweden, in 1855.

This match can only catch fire by being rubbed against a special surface, the reason being that part of the necessary chemicals are on the match head and the other on the striking board. Production of these began in the same year in Sweden and by the firm of Bryant & May in England.

Book matches (using John Walker's original cardboard idea) were devised by an American, Joshua Pusey, in 1892, and were first manufactured in 1896.

═══════ Metric System ═══════

By the time of the French Revolution, France had many different weights and measures that in 1790 the National Assembly decided to reform all of this and produce one standard for the whole country.

Previously each district seemed to have its own unit of length, and each trade its own method of measurement.

The Academy of Sciences set up a committee under the chairmanship of Joseph-Louis Lagrange, a mathematician. He proposed the decimal system and would accept no argument against it. So the commission decided that the unit of weight was to be the *gram*, the weight of a cubic centimetre of water. They also decided that the 'natural' unit of length was to be a ten-millionth of the distance from the Equator to the North Pole, measured on a line which passed through Paris. They called this the *metre*, from the Greek word *metron*, meaning 'measure'. One hundred centimetres were going to be a metre, and ten millimetres were going to make a centimetre.

But then there were two problems. For one

thing the Revolution was still going on, and for another somebody had to find out how far it was from the Equator to the North Pole.

Two people, Jean-Baptiste Delambre and Pierre Méchain, using instruments designed by Jean-Charles de Borda, a designer of navigational and surveying instruments, worked for seven years trying to find out that distance.

They did this by finding the difference in latitude between Barcelona in Spain and Dunkerque in France and so calculating exactly how long a metre should be.

By the time Delambre had finished in 1801 (Méchain had died in 1804) Napoleon was the ruler of France, and he accepted at last the final results as the measurements to use.

# Microscope

Zacharias Jansen, a maker of spectacles, invented the first microscope about 1590, by using a concave and a convex lens together (a concave lens curves inwards, while a convex one bulges outwards). An Italian astronomer and mathematician, Galilei Galileo, then improved Jansen's invention and used it as a scientific instrument, such as to examine the eye of an insect.

But it was Anthony van Leeuwenhoek, a linen merchant of Delft, Holland (1632 to 1723), who really developed the microscope from its primitive beginnings. In his spare time he had the hobbies of glass-blowing and fine metal work, and eventually devised a way of grinding lens accurately, setting them in frames to form microscopes – quite powerful ones, too. For instance, he was the first person ever to see bacteria. (*See* TELESCOPE).

# Microwave Oven

Microwave cooking was quite impossible until 1940, when Sir John Randall and Dr H. A. H. Boot, of Birmingham University, invented the magnetron, for use with Britain's radar system during the Second World War.

There was no intention at all of using it for cooking. What a magnetron does is produce electro-magnetic waves which are only 12 centimetres long and which have a frequency of 2,450 microseconds – very short and fast waves, in fact.

Then it was found that in a cooker, if the food is bombarded with these radio waves, molecular activity and so heat created, and so the food gets cooked quickly.

The first oven using this principle was produced by Raytheon Incorporated, of America, in 1945–47, but it became enormously popular throughout America and Europe from about 1980 when people realised that a microwave oven could be used either for cooking very quickly and cheaply, or for heating pre-cooked food.

# Milk Bottle

These were introduced by the Echo Farms Dairy Company, of New York, in 1879. A bottle with a wired-on cap was made in 1884 by George

Barham, of the Express Dairy, in England. It was not a success.

A decade on, Arthur Hailwood demonstrated his stoppered bottles in Manchester, but it was not until 1906 that fresh milk began to be sold in bottles in Britain, from the Manor Farm Dairy in East Finchley.

The milk bottle cap made of aluminium foil was invented by Josef Jonssen, of Sweden, in 1914. These did not appear in Britain until 1929. Until then, almost all milk was delivered in large churns out of which the milkman would measure out the amount of milk each house required.

# Motor Car

Étienne Lenoir, a Belgian enameller who changed his job to become an engineer, lived in Paris and invented electric brakes, a railway signalling system and, in 1862, the first motor car.

It took him a whole year after that to become confident enough to drive it on a public road, in September 1863, at four miles an hour!

His engine ran on liquid hydrocarbon. He had invented engines which ran on the same compound before. These were much too big, and so it was not until 1862 that he had made one small enough to fit into his vehicle. After this project he gave up inventing cars.

The first petrol-engined car came in 1883, made by Eduard Delamare-Deboutteville, who lived at Fontaine-le-Bourg, France. His first model had iron-tyred wheels and risked being shaken apart. The second model had rubber tyres and was a three-wheeler, but the engine was too heavy and thus collapsed. Having failed, he gave up inventing motor cars, too.

The first successful petrol-engined car was made by Karl Benz, of Mannheim, Germany, in 1885, the three-cylinder engine drove the two rear wheels, and it had a differential gear. It was driven in public for the first time in 1886 at a little over nine miles an hour.

At the same time, Gottlieb Daimler, of Cannstatt, Germany, produced the first four-wheeled car (also run in public for the first time in 1886). From then on both firms continued to develop various cars until the firm of Diamler-Benz came about by uniting the two companies in 1926. Daimler and Benz, however, never actually met each other. Benz was the first to manufacture cars to sell to the public.

The famous Mercedes-Benz cars were introduced in 1901, named after Karl's daughter, whose name was Mercedes. (*See* DIESEL ENGINE *and* PETROL ENGINE).

# ═══ Motor Cycle ═══

In 1885 the first motor cycle was built by Gottlieb
Daimler. It was ridden by his son, Paul – for
six miles. Daimler's original intention was not to
make motor bikes.

The first bike was build as a testing machine
for the newly-invented petrol engine, fitted into
a wooden cycle frame.

The first motor cycle to be manufactured for
sale to the public did not appear until 1894. It
was made by the firm of Hildebrand Wolfmuller,
of Munich, Germany, in the same year as Alex-
andre Darracq, of France, began to manufacture
them too.

# ═══ Motorway ═══

The Avus autobahn in Berlin was the first real
motorway. Although originally planned in 1909
it opened in 1921. It was the idea of Karl Fritsch,
who wanted it to be both a roadway and a race-
track. Eventually it was decided it should just be
a fast dual carriageway.

In Italy, an autostrada opened between Milan
and Varese in 1924. By 1932 Italy had 330 miles
of autostrada, while Germany had 1,000 miles of
autobahns by 1938. The United States opened its
first motorway in 1925, and Holland in 1939.

It was a long time before the idea of the
motorway was accepted in Britain. The first was
*not* the M1, which had its first section opened in
1959, but part of the M6, in 1958.

# Neon Light

Neon lighting is the coloured lighting used for some advertising signs, but the original idea of Georges Claude, who invented it in 1910, was to use his new type of light for homes, offices and so on.

The snag was that its colour turned out to be bright red, when Claude passed an electrical discharge through a tube containing the 'inert gas', neon.

Red lights were not wanted in people's homes, but Jacques Fonseque, who worked in advertising, persuaded Claude that his invention would be excellent if used for illuminated signs instead.

In Paris (1912) a barber's shop announced its name in neon lights and the very first neon advertisement appeared, advertising Cinzano. Success was now certain, and after that other colours were able to be used – starting with blue by adding different powders to coat the inside of the glass tube of the lamps.

From Claude's original neon lights developed the 'gas discharge' lamps used in street lighting – the sodium-vapour lamps which glow orange-yellow, and the mercury-vapour lamps which glow pale blue. (*See* FLUORESCENT LIGHT).

# Non-stick Pan

Roy Plunkett, of the Du Pont Company, of America, discovered a plastic called poly-tetra-fluor-ethylene in 1938, while working on something else. It turned out to be a good insulator against electricity, was not affected by heat or cold, and was very slippery.

In France, an angler called Mark Grégoire tried out some of this plastic to see if it would prevent his fishing-line from sticking. It did!

Having succeeded, his wife then told him to put some of it on to her cooking pans to prevent food from sticking to them. He did just that – and in 1955 founded the Tefal Company.

In Britain, Philip Harben was a cookery expert on television. In one show, being transmitted 'live', an egg stuck to the frying-pan. Since Harben didn't want that to happen again he began to use the plastic, too, and Harbenware was the result, in 1956.

The same plastic is now known as Teflon, Fluon or Hostaflon. (*See* PLASTIC).

# Parachute

The very first design for a parachute was drawn by the 15th century genius Leonardo da Vinci in 1485, but of course he had no way of trying it out, so nothing came of it. In 1783 L. S. Lenormand, a Frenchman, was the first man to demonstrate it in action, jumping from a high tower.

It was in 1797 that Andre-Jacques Garnerin released himself from underneath a hydrogen balloon over Paris and descended in his parachute invention. This was a sort of large bucket with a ribbed canvas sunshade or parasol seven metres across (23 ft.) over it. It swung so much as it came down he vomited as soon as he landed: the first man to suffer from airsickness!

He decided the reason for all the swinging about was that air could not escape, so for his second jump cut a small hole in the top of the canvas and found it to be much better.

Eleven years later, in 1808, Garnerin's invention had to be used in an emergency for the first time, over Warsaw, Poland. A Montgolfier balloon caught fire and the balloonist, Joraki Kurapento, had to jump for it – successfully.

But the first parachute jump from an aeroplane was in 1912, over Jefferson Barracks, St Louis, USA, by Albert Berry, a stunt parachute jumper. Berry's parachute had a line attached to the aircraft to pull it open. In the same year, still in the United States, F. R. Law jumped using a ripcord type of parachute, known as the 'Stevens Life Pack'. In 1919 Leslie Irvin, again in America, made the first descent in his improved rip-cord parachute, which was the real forerunner of all modern ones.

# Paraffin – *Kerosene*

Auguste Laurent, of France, obtained paraffin
first in 1830 by distilling bitumen. Meanwhile
Carl Reichenbach, of Germany, produced it from
wood-tar, and he was the one to give the substance the name of paraffin from *parum affinis*
(because the carbon molecules in it had 'few and
weak affinities').

No one knowing quite what to do with it, it was
suggested in 1839 that it would be very good for
making candles. This was because paraffin at the
time was a solid, not a liquid.

Paraffin wax was used in candles from about
1854. However, James Young, of Scotland, in
1850, found a way of 'obtaining paraffine oil'. He
heated lumps of coal, distilled the vapour and
separated it into naphtha, domestic oil, lubri-
cating oil, heavy fuel oil – and paraffin as we
know it today.

In 1859 Robert Bell, also from Scotland,
managed to produce it from shale. Nowadays it
is produced from crude oil along with diesel fuel,
petrol, etc.

By 1861 the paraffin lamp had been invented
and became very popular as it was cheaper and
safer to use than candles.

# Parking-meter

Carl Magee, editor of an Oklahoma newspaper,
was responsible for the parking-meter. He
became the chairman of a committee set up to
investigate parking problems in the city in 1932.

He thought it would be a good idea to limit the time for which motorists could park, and make them pay for parking at the same time. So he invented the parking-meter.

They went into use for the first time in Oklahoma on 16th July, 1935. These were introduced into Britain in 1958.

The first traffic warden was appointed in 1960 to ensure that motorists used them properly.

# Pasteurization

Pasteurization is named after Louis Pasteur, a French chemist, who worked on the problem between 1857 and 1862.

The original difficulty had nothing to do with milk, though. Pasteur was investigating why French wine and beer was fermenting too quickly.

He found that the cause was germs and other micro-organisms from the air which were getting into the liquid. Heat, he discovered, killed them. So by raising the temperature of the wine and beer to 57.2°C, the problem was solved.

To save milk from going bad a temperature of 61.6°C was necessary, and that had to be maintained for half an hour.

Pasteurised milk, as a result, lasts longer than milk straight from the cow because many of the germs are killed off – but not all of them. Some 'useful' germs remain, but their action is 'slowed down' if the milk is kept in a refrigerator or some other cool place after pasteurization.

# ═══ Pedestrian Crossing ═══

The pedestrian crossing appeared first in London in 1926. It had a sign on a metal post with the words 'Please cross here', and two white lines painted across the road.

In 1934 Sir Leslie Hore-Belisha, the British Minister of Transport, brought into use a new type of crossing with a flashing orange globe on a striped black and white pole at each side of the road, and studs on the road between the two. They became known as Belisha beacons.

As the beacons were made of glass, they were easily broken (by anyone with a catapult), so in 1952 the glass was replaced with plastic.

The first zebra crossings came into use in 1951, replacing the Belisha crossings – with much stronger laws for motorists concerning them.

# ═══ Penicillin ═══

Dr Alexander Fleming, of St Mary's Hospital, London, in 1928 discovered penicillin by accident. He went on holiday leaving some bacteria growing on a jelly he needed for research. On his return he found that a mould had started to grow on the jelly – and it had killed off all his bacteria.

He investigated why a mould should do this to germs, found out why, and made a report on the amazing discovery of 'penicillium'.

Although he used his new discovery to treat and cure a badly infected patient in 1929 (and a Dr Paine, of the Royal Infirmary, Sheffield, did even better with two children in 1930), for some strange reason no real interest was shown in the new drug for more than 10 years. Then Howard Walter Florey and Ernst Chain, in Australia, found a way to produce pure penicillin, and manufactured it in 1941. Since then it has saved thousands of lives. Sir Alexander Fleming, Sir Howard Florey and Dr Ernst Chain were awarded the Nobel prize in 1945 for their work.

## Petrol Engine

Étienne Lenoir invented the first internal-combustion engine that worked, using illuminating gas (liquid hydrocarbon) in 1860.

When Nikolaus Otto, a German travelling salesman, saw the Lenoir engine he realised that the biggest problem was to control the amount of gas and air going into the cylinders so that the engine would always run smoothly.

In 1875 he suddenly got the idea of how to control it by watching smoke coming out of a chimney thickly, then thinning as it spread into the air.

The result was that Otto invented the 'four-stroke' engine. However, it used a flame to ignite the gas and air mixture, even though Siegfried Marcus, of Austria, had already invented a carburettor to turn liquid petrol into a gas in 1867.

Gottlieb Daimler and Karl Benz then, quite independently of each other, developed from Otto's invention the petrol engine for the modern car and motor cycle, which needed an ignition system to make the fuel burn inside the cylinder and so move the piston up and down. (*See* MOTOR CAR *and* DIESEL ENGINE).

# ═══ Petrol Pump ═══

The introduction of the petrol pump had nothing to do with motoring. Sylvanus F. Bowser, of Indiana, USA, found that a kerosene (paraffin) barrel, which stood next to the butter at Jake Gumper's shop, leaked and so was flavouring the butter.

So Bowser set about inventing a pump to provide the paraffin – which was used as lamp oil – in measured amounts. In 1885 he came up with a leak-proof tank, an outlet pipe, and a piston which when pumped would deliver exactly one gallon. Bowser's first pump made especially for use with petrol was not made until 1905.

The first Bowser pump to have a dial showing how much petrol had been served was introduced in 1925. The first that showed the total cost of the petrol served was in 1932.

# ═══ Piano ═══

The harpsichord was like a piano in many ways except that when the keys were pressed, the strings inside were plucked instead of struck.

Bartolommeo Cristofori, of Italy, invented a musical instrument rather like a harpsichord in 1709, except that he used little hammers to hit the strings. Once a hammer had hit a string, it immediately returned to its resting position ready to be used again – and this was the first piano.

What was more, while a harpsichord player had no control over the volume of the sound which he was making, now a player of this new instrument could make the notes either louder or quieter, depending on how hard he hit the keys – pianoforte ('soft-hard') in fact, which was how the piano obtained its name.

The first pianos after Cristofori's were made in Germany by the organ-builder Gottfried Silberman. Later Johann Stein improved the mechanism; then in 1783 John Broadwood, in England, added the piano pedals; in 1821 Sebastien Erard, of France, improved the mechanism further. Heinrich Steinway, of Germany, produced a new arrangement of the strings, known as 'over-strung' in 1855.

The modern piano was now in its present form.

# Plastic

Alexander Parkes, a professor at Birmingham University, experimented with gun cotton (nitrocellulose) and camphor to produce a hard, flexible and transparent material which he called Parkesine – the first plastic material (1850). A use was not found for it, however, until an American, John Hyatt, thought it might be useful for making billiard balls more cheaply, in 1869. He improved it, and found how to manufacture it efficiently, changing its name to celluloid. Twenty years later, in 1889, George Eastman used celluloid to make photographic film for his Kodak cameras. (*See* FILM).

The next important step was in 1904, when a Belgian scientist working in America, Leo Baekeland, produced a plastic from formaldehyde (now known as methanal) and phenol. One story is that he accidentally poured some formaldehyde

over his cheese sandwiches and was surprised by
what happened to his cheese. (On the other hand,
he could have based his experiments on some
made a few years earlier by two German chemists, Krische and Spitteler.) He called his new
material bakelite. It was very hard and heat-
resistant, unlike celluloid which burst into flames
easily.

Then in 1908 Jacques Brandenburger, of Switzerland, who had been trying for years to invent
a waterproof covering for foodstuffs, succeeded in
making a thin film from viscose, and called it
Cellophane. (*See* MAN-MADE FIBRE)

# Pneumatic Tyre

Initially tyres were made of iron.

It was Scottish engineer R. W. Thompson, of
London, in 1845, who made the first rubber tyres.
They were quieter than those of metal, but not
much better – because they were just solid
rubber.

Then in 1888 John Boyd Dunlop, a Scottish
veterinary surgeon working in Belfast, Northern
Ireland, became annoyed when his son's tricycle
left deep grooves in the garden and on the lawn.
So, to protect his garden, he took a length of
garden hose, filled it with water, blocked off the
ends and fitted those on to the tricycle wheels.

Sir John Fagan, who was there at the time,
suggested that filling the hose with air would be
better than water. With this, Dunlop made a tyre
of sheet-rubber which was possible to inflate with
a football pump.

Four months later he fitted the first pair of such

tyres to the rear wheels of the tricycle. Finding that they worked, he bought himself a bicycle and tried the tyres out on it.

What Dunlop had actually done was to re-invent something he had never heard of – the pneumatic tyre. Lord Loraine had the tyres fitted to his carriage in 1847. They were so expensive to make, however, that few people bothered to use them.

The first pneumatic tyres to be fitted to a motor car were made by Edouard Michelin, a cycle-tyre manufacturer, of Paris, who used them on a Daimler car he was driving in the Paris-Bordeaux motor race of 1895.

# Potato Crisp

There was an American Indian called George Crum, who was the chef at the Lake House Hotel, Saratoga Springs, New York. In 1853 he was asked for French fries (called chips in England), but the customer wanted them to be much thinner than usual.

The result – the potato crisp, known originally as Saratoga chips. The idea immediately caught on and people cooked them in their own kitchens. They even packed and sold them from their homes.

An Englishman, Mr Carter, first encountered them in France, and in 1913 decided to manu-facture them in Britain. One member of his work-force, Frank Smith, decided to leave and set up his own business making the same product, in 1920. A few years later Smith's Crisps bought out Carter's business.

# Pressure-cooker

The pressure-cooker was invented in 1679. Denis Papin demonstrated his 'steam digester' at the Royal Society in London in that year.

It was a container with a lid which fitted very tightly and so increased the pressure inside and made water boil at a much higher temperature than usual. He even fitted a safety valve so that the whole thing would not blow up.

Sir Christopher Wren, also a member of the Royal Society, arranged that Papin should write a booklet about it.

The device became known in industry as an autoclave, but was not used again for cooking purposes (which is what Papin had in mind in the first place) until the 20th century, when it first went on the market in America. About the time of the Second World War it became much more popular, when it was realised that pressure-cookers saved fuel (because the normal cooking time was much reduced) and the food being cooked kept its original flavour.

# Radar

A radar system that worked was first developed by Rudolph Kuhnold, of the German Navy's signals research department, in 1933, and demonstrated in 1934.

Kuhnold's work was developed from various sources, including Heinrich Hertz's discovery in the 1880s that electromagnetic waves were being reflected back from the walls of his laboratory, Nikola Tesla's suggestion of 1900 that moving ships might be discovered from radio reflections, Edward Appleton's transmission of radio waves to bounce back from the 'Appleton layer' in the sky in 1924 . . . and so on.

But in 1935 Sir Robert Watson-Watt was asked by the British Government to look into the possibility of inventing a death ray. He found this was not possible, and in any case before using one first you would have to find where your enemy was – so he concentrated on that.

Experiments with bats, which could fly in total darkness without hitting anything, showed that they made very high-pitched noises with their mouths then, from the sound which bounced back off objects, could work out exactly where those objects were. Watson-Watt did some calculations which showed that if electromagnetic waves – radio waves, in fact – were 'bounced back' from moving aircraft then their exact position could be found. The first demonstration took place in the same year, 1935, and by 1939 a complete chain of radar stations were in operation.

The word *radar* was invented by S. M. Tucker, of the US Navy, in 1940. The radar system is now widely employed in sea and air navigation.

# Radio

The first radio signal was transmitted in 1866, by Mahlon Loomis, of Washington, DC, USA, who succeeded in sending messages over 19 kilometres (14 miles), and in 1872 erected the first pair of permanent radio masts. Many others were involved in the early experiments, including Heinrich Hertz, who showed that electromagnetic waves could travel at the speed of light. From this 'radiation' came the word 'radio'.

Then from 1894 the half-British, half-Italian electrical engineer Guglielmo Marconi began his experiments, at the age of 21. Within a year he had sent radio waves from a transmitter on one side of a hill to a receiver out of sight on the other, near Bologna, Italy.

The Italian Government was not interested, so Marconi turned to the British for help instead. The Post Office was interested, but not the British Government, so in 1897 Marconi and his British relatives set up the Wireless Telegraph & Signal Company (which changed its name to the Marconi Wireless Telegraph Company in 1900).

They concentrated on fitting radios to ships. Then on 12th December, 1901, Marconi sent the letter 'S' in Morse code (three dots) from his radio station at Poldhu Point in Cornwall, and it was received in Newfoundland – the first transatlantic broadcast.

Marconi did have other radio transmitters – the first being set up at the Needles Hotel, Alum Bay, Isle of Wight, in 1897.

Until this time all radio transmissions had been in Morse code. In 1906, though, the first radio broadcast using a microphone took place, by

Reginald Aubrey at Brant Rock, Massachusetts, USA.

The first regular broadcasts were transmitted experimentally in New York in 1907, by the Lee de Forest Radio Telephone Company, and the first programme of gramophone records, to entertain steamers on the Great Lakes, was transmitted by Thomas Clark, of Detroit, in 1907.

The BBC first broadcast at 6 p.m. on 14th November, 1922, from Station 2LO at Marconi House, The Strand, London. It consisted of just a news bulletin.

The BBC was the British Broadcasting Company in those days; it did not become the British Broadcasting Corporation until later.

# Railway

The first railway of any sort appears to have been opened in 1789 at Loughborough, Leicestershire, by William Jessop, but little is now known about it.

Another Jessop railway, for carrying goods, was the Surrey Iron Railway, which opened in London in 1803. These both had wagons pulled by mules or donkeys.

The first steam locomotive, though, ran near Merthyr Tydfil, in Wales, in 1804, and a few days later passengers were travelling in a carriage pulled by it. Both were inventions of Richard Trevithick, a Cornish engineer.

Four months afterwards the Oystermouth Railway opened to carry passengers from Swansea, Wales, to Oystermouth, but this was horse-drawn.

In 1825 the Stockton and Darlington Railway opened, a 27-mile track and the first *public* railway to be operated by steam locomotives.

The locomotive pulled both goods and passenger wagons at the same time to form the train. In 1830 the first regular passenger service pulled by steam traction (a stationary engine for four miles because the gradient was so steep, and a locomotive for two miles where the track was more or less level) was the Canterbury and Whitstable Railway.

In the same year the first passenger railway pulling steam locomotives only was the Liverpool and Manchester Railway.

Open wagons were used until enclosed carriages appeared in 1834.

The first diesel locomotive was used on the Prussian-Hessian State Railway service in 1912, but it was not a great success. Much more successful were the Swedish-built diesel-electric locomotives used by the Tunisian Railways in 1921.

Electric trains, using overhead cables to provide the power, appeared much earlier. The first went into operation with the Baltimore and Ohio Railroad, USA, in 1894.

=== Refrigerator ===

How to keep food cool, especially wine and drinks, was explained by Blasius Villafranca in 1550. (*See* ICE-CREAM).

In 1834, Jacob Perkins, however, (an American living in London), discovered a new way of keeping food cold by inventing a 'vapour compression cycle' of operations, in which a 'volatile liquid' was evaporated. Then the vapour condensed, evaporated again, and so on.

At the same time James Harrison, a Scot who had emigrated to Australia in 1837, was working on a similar idea, except that the liquid which he used was ammonia. His machines were successful and were among the first to be sold commercially (1851).

In America, Alexander Twining was experimenting with ether vapour, and in 1850 was producing 2,000 pounds of ice a day in Cleveland, Ohio.

Refrigerators were first designed for use in industry, however, not for use in people's homes. The first refrigerator designed for home use was the Domelre, electrically-operated and made in Chicago in 1913. Domestic refrigerators were made by Frigidaire and first sold in Britain in 1924.

# Rickshaw

The rickshaw – a two-seater, two-wheeled carriage, pulled by a man who runs in front – is obviously Japanese, since that is where rickshaws have been used as a kind of taxi. Now it is more likely to be pulled by a person on a bicycle.

It is not, however, Japanese at all, even though that is the country where it was first used, nor is it a very ancient method of transport.

An American minister of the Baptist Church, the Revd Jonathan Scobie, had a wife who was not able to walk very well. The rickshaw was his invention in 1869 to provide a means of transport for her round the streets of Yokohama.

The first rickshaw operators were those Japanese whom Scobie had converted to Christianity, to provide them with a way of earning a living.

# Roller-skate

The first roller-skate was known to have been worn by Joseph Merlin, a Belgian living in England. In 1760, at a party given at a house in Soho Square, London, he skated into the ballroom playing a violin at the same time!

Unfortunately, since he couldn't stop, or change direction, he roller-skated into a large mirror, broke that, his violin, and injured himself all at the same time.

The next we hear of the roller-skate was when Robert Tyers, of London, invented his Volitos in 1823. With five small wheels lined up one behind the other they were designed, he said, to be attached to boots 'for the purpose of travelling or pleasure'.

But the four-wheeled roller-skate was invented by James Plimpton, of New York, in 1863. The wheels were made of boxwood with rubber padding above them, and as soon as they appeared roller-skating became popular in both America and Europe.

## Safety-pin

The safety-pin is very ancient. Somebody about 2000 BC bent a straight pin double and made the point tuck under a hook or a slot to hold it in place. In those days it was made of bronze.

The trouble was that the end of the pin still kept slipping out, and no one could think of how to fit a spring to make it stay in place – until 1849, that is.

An American inventor, Walter Hunt, owed some money. The lender said he would pay him 400 dollars for all the rights to as many shapes as Hunt could twist an old piece of wire, and so cancel the debt.

It took Walter Hunt three hours one afternoon to earn his 400 dollars.

What he did was add a circular twist where the bend came in a safety-pin. This then acted as a kind of spring which solved the problem of more than three-and-a-half thousand years! Apparently, 400 dollars was all that Hunt made out of his invention.

## Safety Razor

In order to shave off their beards, many things have been tried by men – including rubbing the face with pumice-stone, which was common in the days of Charles II of England.

The so-called 'cutthroat' or 'open' razor had been in use for several centuries, and men were regularly cutting themselves with it – as King Camp Gillette, a salesman of Wisconsin, USA, realised while doing just that when he was shaving himself with one in 1895.

What he also realised was that the only part of the razor which did any work was the cutting edge.

Some years before his employer, William Painter, who had invented and made bottle-caps, said to him, 'Why don't you invent something which will be used once and thrown away? Then the customer will come back for more.'

So, from the memory of that, Gillette suddenly got the idea of a sliver of steel with a very sharp edge to be used in a clamp and then thrown away.

The problem was in making that sliver of sharpened steel, but this was solved by William Nickerson, a mechanic who had already invented the push-button for lifts and whom Gillette was employing on a part-time basis.

The American Safety Razor Company was formed in 1901, Nickerson had completely solved the problem in 1902, and production began in 1903.

The first year's sales were terrible – 51 razors and 168 blades. Obviously Gillette was not going to make a fortune out of that!

Then in 1904 the new idea of a safety razor suddenly became popular, for no obvious reason, with a sale of 90,000 Gillette razors and nearly twelve-and-a-half million razor-blades. Sales started in Britain with equal success the following year.

Gillette realised that his razor-blades were being used more than once, until they became blunt, and not thrown away each time as he had intended.

It was not until 1956 that the old-established

British firm of Wilkinson Sword – which had been making swords (and later garden implements) for centuries – understood the implication of this. As a result they produced the first stainless steel razor-blades which were designed to be used over and over again before they needed to be thrown away. (*See* ELECTRIC RAZOR).

## Seed Drill

Until the invention of the seed drill, the sowing of seed was by 'broadcasting' – exactly the same as in Biblical days, where the farmer or one of his labourers would walk across a field scattering the seed by hand from a tray.

The solution to improve upon this method and so grow more food was obvious – some device to let the seed down tubes at a controlled rate into holes or furrows and then to cover the ground over afterwards. The trouble was no one could invent any machine to do this which actually worked.

Jethro Tull solved the problem in 1701. The seeds were held in a container on a wheeled vehicle and, as it moved along, the wheels made the seed feed out down hollow tubes, into a small furrow cut in front of them, and pulled behind the vehicle was a harrow which covered the soil back over where the seed had been dropped.

The biggest problem was to control the flow of the seed, of course. Jethro Tull solved this by making use of the mechanism on his local church organ, copying that to use a brass cover and an adjustable spring.

# Sewing-machine

The right sort of needle had to be invented first. It was not until 1755 that Charles Weisenthal, an Englishman, invented a double-pointed needle with an eye in the centre.

Thomas Saint then, in 1790, devised a sewing-machine to use in the making of boots and shoes. It was very similar to a modern sewing-machine, but did not use Weisenthal's needle, and so was soon forgotten.

In 1830, though, Barthélemy Thimonnier, a tailor of Amplepuis, near Saint-Etienne in France, invented a sewing-machine largely out of wood, using Weisenthal's needle, which was all too successful.

Other tailors, who all worked by hand, thought this machine would put them out of work, so they organised a mob to wreck Thimonnier's workshop. He escaped with just one machine.

Then in 1845 a manufacturer offered to make his latest model for him, but using metal instead of wood. A number of these machines were made and put into operation to make Army uniforms, but the news got round again and this time a much larger mob completely destroyed the premises within three years, and production stopped altogether, never to restart.

Thimonnier died in poverty in 1857.

However, several people began to manufacture sewing-machines elsewhere after Thimonnier's first invention of it – Elias Howe, for example, inventor of a lock-stitch machine. He was an American who went to London, and sold his invention to a corset manufacturer for whom he later worked in 1846.

But the man who invented and produced the first successful sewing-machine for use in people's homes was Isaac Merritt Singer, of Boston, USA.

He made use of the eye-pierced needle, the pressing surfaces to hold the cloth used by Elias Howe, the perpendicular movement of the needle, and the overhanging arm – all of which, apart from the needle of that type, had been used in Thomas Saint's original design. Singer sewing-machines began selling in 1851.

In 1889 the Singer Manufacturing Company produced the first electric sewing-machine.

## Sponsored Walk

In 1959 Kenneth Johnson wanted some way of raising money for the World Refugee Fund. He thought of the idea of a walk from Letchworth, Hertfordshire, where he lived, to Yatesbury, Wiltshire.

He charged an entry fee of 5p, and everyone joining in was supposed to gather sponsors to pay them a fixed sum of each mile walked.

Twenty-one people finally took part, and the event raised about £20. It was not entirely a success, though, because the distance was too far. No one succeeded in walking all the way, but the final three walkers, including Johnson, gave up after 50 miles at Ewelme, Oxfordshire.

105

# Steam-engine

To pump water out of Coneygre Colliery, Thomas Newcomen built the first working steam-engine at Tipton, Staffordshire, in 1712. It had taken him 10 years of experimenting before his engine finally worked, and originally he had intended to use it to pump water out of the Cornish tin mines. Cornwall however, had no coal – it had to be brought in by sea at great cost – and Newcomen's engine, in order to work, needed a great deal of it.

There were plenty of coal mines in and near Staffordshire, however, so that was where it was first used. The importance of Newcomen's invention was that with this pump to keep the mines clear of water, coal could be mined from much deeper levels than before.

James Watt improved the steam-engine by making it more efficient. He did this by making the steam condense in a separate closed container instead of in the cylinder, and used steam at low pressure to move the piston.

George Stephenson was the greatest designer of steam-engines for railway locomotives – his Locomotive Number 1 pulled the first train on the Stockton and Darlington Railway in 1825. (*See* RAILWAY).

# Steam Turbine

In an ordinary steam-engine, the piston moves up and down (or in and out) by means of a connecting rod and crankshaft powered by the pressure of the steam.

A great deal of energy is therefore used in making those parts move. It would be much more efficient if a jet of steam could be made to turn a wheel directly, like water pouring on to a water-wheel, a kind of revolving engine.

The problem always was that the wheel would have to be made to turn very quickly indeed if the engine were to be successful, and of any real use.

This was not possible until 1884, when improved technology – in this case the invention of tough steel – came about. The Honourable Charles Parsons, youngest son of the Earl of Rosse and trained as an engineer, designed a series of vanes attached to wheels on a shaft.

The wheels on which the vanes were set were larger the farther away they were from the jet of steam – because obviously the farther away they were the less the effect of the jet would be on them, so they needed to increase in size.

Then he made steam pass from one to the other. In that way, each vane was using part of the energy from the steam.

Parsons achieved astonishing speed in his engine. Even his first turbine revolved at 18,000 revolutions per minute, and shortly he was to improve on that.

Parsons turbines were soon in use on ships which included the first large passenger liners, because they were so much faster than ordinary steam-engines and a great deal more efficient, hence cheaper to run.

This was not Parson's original intention, though, for he had expected his invention to be used for generating electricity – so he also made a dynamo which could be driven at equally high speeds.

Parsons turbines are still the main sources of electricity throughout the world.

# Stethoscope

René T. H. Laennec, of Quimper, Brittany, was working in Paris in 1816 as a pathologist and expert on heart-disease, at the Necher Hospital.

However, there was no easy way of listening to the way a heart was beating at the time, until he came up with a very simple solution – which surprisingly no one had thought of before.

First, he rolled up a piece of paper, tied it with string so that it had a hole down the centre, then put his ear at one end, the other end over the patient's heart, and listened.

After many experiments to improve his idea, he made himself a wooden cylinder, 30 centimetres long, 3 cms in diameter, and with a hole right through it 5 mm in diameter.

So that it would fit more easily into his pocket, he made the tube in two parts and then put the parts together when he wanted to use it.

He himself died of heart-disease within 10 years, unfortunately.

The modern version of the stethoscope, with a tube going into each ear, and all of it flexible, was introduced about 1855.

A simple stethoscope, not very different in design from Laennec's, is still used by midwives for listening to the heartbeat of a baby while it is still inside the mother.

# Submarine

The first submarine carried 12 people who rowed it along with oars protruding through watertight holes.

It had a wooden frame covered in greased leather, and was demonstrated in front of King James I of England for two hours underwater in 1624. It was invented by Cornelius Drebbel, a Dutchman living in London.

The next submarine known to have been built was a one-man midget submarine, driven by a propeller, in 1776. David Bushnell, of America, invented it for attacking British ships during the American War of Independence. The propeller was operated by turning a handle.

The man inside it, Sergeant Ezra Lee, managed to fasten a mine to Earl Howe's flagship in New York harbour, but the mine floated away and no damage was done.

Still in America, in 1864 during the Civil War, a Confederate submarine with a crew of eight and armed with a torpedo of sorts sank a Union ship. Both vessels blew up. This submarine was fitted with a hand-operated propeller.

There had been a submarine driven by compressed air at Rochefort, France, in 1863. That weighed 420 tons but had too slow a speed

and too small a range to be of any use to the French Navy.

In 1879 the Russian Navy had 50 submarines designed for coastal defence, but the first seagoing, self-propelled submarine was built in Sweden and designed by a clergyman from Liverpool called Samuel Garratt. This was steam-driven, as were the first British-made Garratt submarines built in 1887 for the Turkish Navy.

John Holland, though, was the originator of the modern submarine. He designed one to be used by the Irish against the British Navy, and by 1889 had improved this into almost its modern form. It was used by the US Navy in 1900, and by the Royal Navy in 1901.

The first nuclear-powered submarine was the Nautilus (named after the one in Jules Verne's book *Twenty Thousand Leagues Under The Sea*). It was designed by Admiral Hyman Rickover, of the US Navy, and was launched on the River Thames in January 1954. Its first sea trials were in January 1955, and she was refuelled for the first time two years and 69,138 miles later. (*See* TORPEDO).

# Supermarket

Until 1912, assistants served the customers in all shops, but in that year two self-service stores were opened in California, USA, followed by a chain of self-service grocery stores.

Four years later, in 1916, the first of such stores to have check-outs was the Piggly Wiggly Stores in Memphis, Tennessee, USA, belonging to Clarence Saunders.

These shops were not very large. The first store to be regarded, because of its size, as a real supermarket was the King Kullen Food Store, which was opened by Michael Cullen on Long Island, USA, in 1930.

# Table Tennis

Table tennis is an example of a change of name causing something to become popular.

James Gibb, one of the founders of the Amateur Athletics Association, some time in the 1890s invented a game for wet days to be played on the dining-room table at his house in Croydon, England. For bats he used cigar-box lids, and for balls he used champagne corks. He tried replacing the corks with rubber balls, but these he found were too heavy for playing the game quickly, so he sent to America to have celluloid balls made specially for him. (*See* PLASTIC).

Gibb was, of course, a wealthy man, but after he had designed some plain wooden bats to go with the celluloid balls he thought he might as well make some money out of the game which he had invented, and had some sets made by John Jacques & Son, Ltd.

In 1898 he began trying to sell them, calling the game 'Gossima'. The only shop selling them was Hamley's, of Regent Street, London, the famous toy shop. They did not sell very well at all, but when he changed the name to 'Ping-Pong' the game immediately became successful.

In 1902 another manufacturer started making bats with a studded rubber surface – Bryan's Atropos Patent Ping-Pong Bat.

The first table tennis club opened in London in 1901, and in the same year the first table tennis tournament was held.

# Telephone

Probably the first telephone was designed by Antonio Meucci, of Havana, Cuba, who in 1849 used his device to talk to his invalid wife, on the third floor of his house, from the basement. He made it himself, but never used in public.

Johann Philip Reis, of Friedrichesdorf, Germany, used a violin case, a hollowed-out bung from a beer barrel and a sausage skin and transmitted speech over a 91.4 metre (300 ft.) line in 1861.

Both of these were, no doubt, something like what can be done now with a couple of empty tins connected by a length of string pulled tight. The sound vibration travels along the string and is amplified by the tins at each end.

Alexander Graham Bell was a Scottish doctor specialising in teaching the deaf to speak.

He was working at Boston University, USA. While experimenting with the possibility of transmitting sound by using electricity – using his microphone to send musical notes over his circuit – he suddenly realised that speech might also be sent in exactly the same way.

So without warning he adjusted the apparatus, then said into the mouthpiece, 'Mr Watson, come here, I want you.' His assistant, Mr Watson, was several rooms away and, to his astonishment, heard him clearly – in March 1876.

Bell demonstrated his invention at the Philadelphia Centennial Exhibition in June of the same year, where most people took little notice of it until, just as astonished as Mr Watson had been, the Emperor of Brazil, Pedro II, suddenly announced, 'My God, it talks!' Success was now assured.

Bell took his invention back to Scotland and demonstrated it at a meeting of the British Association for the Advancement of Science that September. In less than a year the first telephone line between two buildings linked the Queen's Theatre, London, to Canterbury Hall. The first private and business telephones were in use in the USA in April and May 1877, respectively.

In England, the first private telephone call was made on 14th January, 1878, by Queen Victoria to Sir Thomas Biddulph, the Queen in Osborne House, Isle of Wight, and Sir Thomas in Osborne Cottage.

At the age of 30, Alexander Graham Bell was both rich and famous as the Bell telephone began to be sold throughout the world.

# ═══════ Telescope ═══════

Spectacles of one sort or another date from at least the year 1289, but it took until 1608 for a Dutch lens-maker called Hans Lippershey to hold two lenses in line, look through them, and discover that a distant church steeple had become magnified and so apparently closer to him.

Italian astronomer and mathematician Galilei Galileo (*see* MICROSCOPE) heard of this discovery, worked out the reason for why it worked, and made a telescope for use with his own work in astronomy.

Galileo was the first, for example, to discover that the sun was not just a round yellow disc but had mysterious blobs on it, and that one planet had moons moving round it.

Then Johann Kepler suggested that what a

telescope really needed was two convex lenses, and Christopher Scheiner built one for him to his specifications in 1611, mainly so that Kepler could examine the 'sun spots' which Galileo had seen.

He had the sense, though, to use dark glass to protect his eyes from the glare of the sun – unlike Galileo, who eventually went blind largely because of using only plain glass lenses.

Sir Isaac Newton in England realised that early telescopes showed rather blurred images, and that the colours were not accurate.

He had been experimenting with prisms (triangle-shaped chunks of glass) and had discovered that with them white light could be broken up into the colours of the spectrum which formed white light.

Newton knew now that the reason for the faults in the early telescopes were being caused by glass separating the colours wrongly, so he invented a reflecting telescope, where a mirror replaced one of the lenses – the basis of modern astronomical telescopes and of binoculars.

## Television

There was not just one inventor of television. Experiments had been carried out in 1862 by the Abbé Caselli, an Italian priest living in France, who invented a system of transmitting pictures of handmade drawings and written messages.

In 1881 Shelford Bidwell, an Englishman, was able to demonstrate an early form of television which used a cell of selenium (a photoelectric cell) moving up and down mechanically in a box. But he thought that the only way to produce a good picture was to make use of 90,000 photoelectric cells, each attached by a separate wire – and that was beyond him.

A Scottish electrical engineer, Alan Campbell-Swinton, hearing of Bidwell's experiments and knowing that Ferdinand Braun, of Austria, had invented the cathode ray oscilloscope (rather like a modern television tube, but designed for showing electrical waves), put the two ideas together.

He realised that an electronic switch was needed to switch on the photoelectric cells in turn, and that the oscilloscope tube could be used to receive pictures.

He also designed a camera to go with it, which stored the light falling on to the photoelectric cells so that when it was switched on all the variations of light were transmitted at the same time.

That was in 1911, and became the basis of the television system which went into operation by the BBC at Alexandra Palace, London, in 1936.

Meanwhile, in Russia, Boris Rosing had invented his own television apparatus in 1907 which did not work very well. But one of Rosing's students, Vladimir Zworykin, left Russia for America in 1919, and invented his camera tube which used Campbell-Swinton's storage of light principle in 1923. His first pictures were still not very good, but by 1928 he had improved the system considerably.

John Logie Baird, working in London, gave his demonstration of 'real' television in 1926. This was the first proper television picture ever transmitted, but Baird was using a mechanical system

116

instead of an electrical one (although he developed an electronic receiver later).

The race was then on between the RCA Company, of America, and Marconi-EMI, of England, to develop television. The Marconi-EMI team, under Isaac Schoenberg, solved the final problems with the invention of the Emitron camera in 1934.

Meanwhile, John Logie Baird was still working on his television system. In 1928 he produced the first television picture in colour rather than in black-and-white, the high-definition colour television picture in 1938, and in 1941 the large-screen colour television receiver.

Unfortunately, he always refused to accept that electronic transmission of pictures was essential, rather than mechanical methods, so none of his inventions are now present in modern television sets.

# Toilet-paper

In Roman times a sponge on a stick was used in public toilets and kept in a pot of salt water when not in use. When travelling, Romans carried pieces of cloth with them, which they would wedge into the cleft end of a stick when they needed to use it.

In medieval times, well-off people in Europe used pieces of blanket, and monks would cut up their worn-out habits into squares.

In Asia, Hindus and Moslems simply used their left hand – and washed it afterwards with water from a jug – thus giving rise to the custom of strict Hindus and Moslems of never eating food with their left hand!

The first toilet-paper was probably Gayety's Medicated Paper, of New Jersey, USA, in 1857, sold in packs of 500 sheets of shiny paper.

Rolls of paper first appeared in 1882 in America, but already in England the British Perforated Paper Company was in 1880 producing rolls of paper aimed originally for use in barbers' shops for the wiping of cutthroat razors. For some strange reason these rolls were *not* perforated – people just tore off a piece as they needed it.

Jeyes, of England, were producing flat packs of interleaved toilet tissue in the 1890s. Before, during and after this time, people who couldn't afford to buy anything special for the lavatory made do with such things as torn-up newspaper.

The Scott brothers, of America, brought out the first toilet-roll with a brand name in 1899. It was called the Waldorf. (The firm later joined with Bowater, of England, to create the firm of Bowater-Scott.)

The first soft toilet-paper probably appeared in 1932, when a Jewish firm fled from Hitler's Germany to set up business in London, and Andrex made the first British soft toilet-paper. Sales of this were not very good, however, until 1945, at the end of the Second World War. (*See* WATER-CLOSET).

# ═══ Toothpaste Tube ═══

Before toothpaste came the toothbrush, which was probably invented in China about 1498, using animal bristles set into a handle.

It was not until about 1648 that something similar appeared in Europe (Paris). Certainly toothbrushes could be bought in Britain in the year 1690, but not until 1938 was it possible to buy a nylon toothbrush, when this was invented by the use of Exton, made by the Du Pont Company, of America – and electric toothbrushes were first made by the Squibb Company, of New York, USA, in 1961.

Toothpaste and tooth-powder used to be packed into round pots and basically consisted of a slightly gritty cleaning material and perhaps a polishing agent (such as jeweller's rouge).

Then in 1841 the American artist, John Rand, invented a tube, sealed at one end and with a cap over the opening at the other, which collapsed if it was pressed or rolled. He designed it for oil-paint, for the use of artists.

The first collapsible toothpaste tube was designed by Washington Sheffield, an American dentist, in 1892, and he established the Sheffield Tube Company to manufacture it.

This was such a good idea, that, in the same year Beechams, of England, copied it and started selling their Beechams Tooth Paste in tubes instead of in pots.

# Torpedo

Robert Whitehead was the British manager of an engineering firm in Italy.

In 1866 he thought up the idea of using a small boat filled with explosives, steering it by wires to an enemy ship, and so blow it up.

From that first, rather unsuccessful basic idea he developed the underwater torpedo. He controlled its depth in the water by means of hydrostatic equipment, which responded to water pressure, and he steered it by using a gyroscope.

It finally appeared for the first time two years later, in 1868. The first torpedo-boat appeared in 1877. (*See* SUBMARINE).

# Traffic-light

The first traffic-lights, showing red and green, were put up outside the Houses of Parliament, London, in 1868.

J. P. Knight, a railway signalling engineer, devised them to be rather like an old-fashioned railway signal, with signalling arms and two gas-lit lamps, one red and one green.

The lights were changed by hand by a policeman, and their purpose was to stop the traffic for Members of Parliament who wanted to cross the road. They were in use for only a year before the gas exploded, injuring the policeman operating the lights.

Modern traffic-lights went into operation in Cleveland, Ohio, USA, in 1914. They showed either green or red, with a warning buzzer sounding when the lights changed. Three-colour lights (red, amber and green) were erected in New York in 1918, controlled by a man who stood in a tall look-out post in the middle of the street.

The French erected traffic-lights in Paris in 1923, with a gong sounding to warn motorists of when the lights were going to change. Traffic-lights returned to London in July 1926.

So far, all the lights were controlled by hand. The first automatic lights were installed in Wolverhampton, England, in 1927.

## Transistor

Before the transistor there were radio valves, invented by Sir Ambrose Fleming who had helped Marconi with his early experiments (*see* RADIO).

He produced his first valve in 1904, when he discovered that if he had a vacuum tube with two electrodes, one heated and one cold, it could detect wireless waves. In 1906 in Vienna, Robert von Lieben, working on the problem of amplifying telephone signals, added a third electrode and found that this would make weak signals very much stronger or louder.

Lee de Forest, of America, was to improve upon that.

Transistors, however, do all that radio valves used to do, but are more reliable, tougher, smaller, and need only a fraction of the electricity required by valves. They were first demonstrated by William Shockley, John Bardeen and Walter Brattain at the Bell Telephone Laboratories, USA, in 1948.

What they discovered was that materials like silicon and germanium neither conducted electricity nor acted as resistors to it.

In fact, they were 'semiconductors'. Silicon is a very commen element in the world, being found in such things as sand, flint and quartz.

Shockley then found that by adding traces of other material to silicon he could affect how the silicon reacted to the passage of electricity through it.

This discovery led to the development of all modern miniature circuits, such as those used in radios, televisions, video-recorders, pocket calculators, computers, and so on. In fact, without the transistor, pocket-calculators and computers, not to mention small personal radios, would have been impossible.

# Typewriter

In 1714 Henry Mill, an Englishman, invented the basic idea of the typewriter, but unfortunately no model at all has survived.

In 1808 Pellegrine Turri, of Italy, invented a sort of typewriter (again, nothing is left of the original) by means of which his blind friend, Countess Fantoni, could write letters.

Those letters are still in existence, evidence that the machine really worked! It's thought that the countess pressed a plunger for each letter to operate it.

William Burt, of Detroit, USA, produced his version of a typewriter in 1828 'which could go almost as fast as one could write with an ordinary pen'.

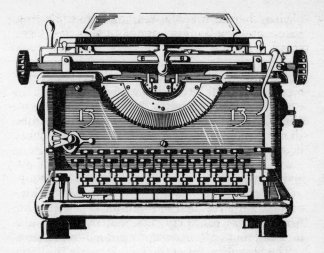

In Denmark, Malling Hansen, of Copenhagen, invented a very heavy machine with 52 keys, and Hansen typewriters were still in use in Europe and America at least until the beginning of the First World War.

The real genius behind the modern typewriter, however, was Christopher Scholes, of Milwaukee, USA. He and Carlos Gliddon had invented a machine which numbered the pages in a book. Gliddon suddenly asked why it was not possible to make a machine which would write letters and words as well, instead of just numbers. So Scholes set about making one.

Scholes's typewriter, when he had invented it, was offered to the Remington Fire Arms Company. This firm had made weapons for use in the American Civil War, and now that was over guns were not in such demand. It had already moved into the manufacture of sewing-machines, typewriters seemed to be a good idea, so the deal was agreed in 1873. The first type-writers went on sale the same year.

Scholes continued to improve the Remington typewriter until 1876, when it was shown at the Philadelphia Centennial Exhibition. It aroused very little interest – because that was the exhibi-tion at which Alexander Graham Bell's telephone made its first public appearance, and most of the attention was concentrated on that. (*See* TELEPHONE).

In desperation, Remington decided to *lend* several hundred of their unsold typewriters to firms so they could try them out. At once, sales took off, and once started, continued to increase.

The arrangement of the keys (exactly the same as we have now on typewriters and computers) was decided by Scholes to solve a problem. The keys kept jamming, so he put the letters which often occurred together in words as far from each other as possible.

# ═══ Underground Railway ═══

It was Charles Pearson, Member of Parliament
for Lambeth, London, who suggested the underground railway in 1846.

Because it took a great deal of time to raise
the money to pay for it, the North Metropolitan
Railway Company was not formed until 1853,
and the first shaft not drilled (at Euston Square,
London) until 1860.

The railway finally opened to carry passengers
in 1863, using steam locomotives. There were
seven stations on the line, and the carriages were
lit by gas.

The first successful *electric* underground
railway, the Tube, opened in 1890, and not only
were the engines electric, but the carriages had
electric lighting as well.

The city of Budapest, Hungary, followed by
opening the first underground railway in Europe
in 1896. The Paris Metro followed in 1900. In
Britain automatic doors appeared in 1922, and
driverless, automatic trains were first tried out
in London in 1964.

# ═══ Vaccination – *Inoculation* ═══

Edward Jenner was a country doctor in Gloucestershire. In those days, smallpox was a deadly disease, very often fatal, and even when it was not it disfigured people's faces by leaving deep scars.

One day he was told by a milkmaid that she would never get smallpox because she had already had cowpox. Cowpox was a disease of the udders of cows.

Jenner thought about what the milkmaid had said and, in 1796, scratched an eight-year-old boy with the pus from a cowpox sore on the arm of another milkmaid.

A similar sore developed on the boy, but he did not become ill, and when a few weeks later Jenner scratched the same boy with smallpox pus – and again some months later – smallpox still did not develop.

It had been a risky experiment, but during the next two years Jenner experimented further with different people, and found what the first milkmaid had said was true, cowpox pus, if scratched into the skin, gave complete protection against the dreaded smallpox.

In 1798 he published his findings at his own expense, and within two more years many other doctors were making use of the new vaccination process (named by Jenner from *vacca*, the Latin for 'cow').

Before Edward Jenner's time, a similar but very risky process had sometimes been used, to put the pus from someone who was suffering from a mild case of smallpox into the skin of someone who was not suffering from it at all, in the hopes that this would prevent smallpox from developing.

Sometimes it had worked, but more often than not it had actually caused the disease to appear.

Since Jenner's time, of course, vaccination has been used to prevent a great variety of diseases from appearing.

# ══ Vacuum Cleaner ══

There had been types of suction cleaners before, usually operated by bellows and needing two people to work them, but in 1901 Herbert C. Booth went to a demonstration of a new cleaner.

It was being used to clean a railway carriage at St Pancras Station, London. Compressed air was used to blow the dust off the floors and seats – and it came up in clouds.

Booth said it would make more sense to suck the dirt out, not blow it away, because all it was doing was settling again. The answer was that it had been tried but didn't work.

Herbert Booth was a bridge-builder, and a designer of Ferris wheels (the 'big wheels' at fairgrounds). When he returned home from the demonstration, he lay on the floor, placed a handkerchief over his mouth, and sucked hard at the carpet. A great deal of dust collected on the handkerchief – and the modern vacuum cleaner was ready to be invented.

Few houses had electricity in those days, (1902). So, when Booth's first machine was ready, he provided a vacuum cleaning service from a horse-drawn machine which stood in the street and had a hose nearly 244 metres (800 ft.) long, so that it could reach anywhere in the house.

The machine was very noisy, so much so that other horses used to bolt with fright when he started it up.

Success really came with the coronation of King Edward VII at Westminster Abbey in 1902. The royal carpets were filthy – after all, Queen Victoria's coronation had taken place in 1837 – time was running out before the coronation took place, so Booth offered to use his new machine and within hours of offering had the carpets clean.

The king was so delighted that he ordered two vacuum cleaners himself, one for Buckingham Palace and one for Windsor Castle.

Booth produced a portable vacuum cleaner for sale to the public in 1906, but was beaten to being the first to do this by Chapman & Skinner, of San Francisco, in 1905.

The upright vacuum cleaner with a dustbag fastened to the handle was invented by Murray Spangler, who was the caretaker of a department store in Canton, Ohio, USA. He made it out of wood and tin, with a broom handle and an old pillowcase. W. H. Hoover saw this, found that it actually worked, however odd it looked, and started producing similar machines in 1907.

Hoover was a harness-maker, whose business was not doing so well since the introduction of the motor car, but by acquiring Spangler's upright machine his name became the one by which vacuum cleaners for the home first became known. (*See* CARPET-SWEEPER).

# ═══ Vacuum Flask – *Thermos* ═══

The vacuum flask started out purely for scientific use. Sir James Dewar needed a container to use in his laboratory to keep very cold liquids, such as liquid air, cold for long periods.

So, in 1892, he invented a glass container with double walls and a space between them, pumped out the air to create a vacuum and then sealed the empty space – because he knew that heat could not pass through a vacuum.

To make extra sure, he had a mirror surface put on the inside of the two layers of glass wall to reduce any possible escape of the cold by radiation.

In 1904 Reinhold Burger, a German, saw Dewer's flask and realised that what kept liquids cold would also keep them hot in exactly the same way. Also, it could be used in people's homes as well as in laboratories.

He offered a prize for the best name to call it, and *Thermos* (Greek for 'hot') won. The Thermos flask was fitted into a container with a stopper and a drinking cup, and went on sale – and has been selling ever since.

# ═══ Video-recorder ═══

The first video recordings were actually made by John Logie Baird (*see* TELEVISION) in 1928, using gramophone discs which were fed through his Televisor.

But the use of tape did not appear until 1956, when Alexander Poniatoff demonstrated his

Ampex machine in Chicago – and used it for a pre-recorded television broadcast as well.

Within two years, RCA announced their video-recorder, but in 1967 Ampex developed a video recording system which used a metal disc rather than a reel of tape, which was able to locate and play back any part of a programme in less than four seconds — the beginning of 'instant replay' as on television sports programmes.

There are three systems in use at the moment for home use – the VHS system, developed by Sony, the Beta system developed by Sanyo (both of Japan), and the '2000' system developed by Philips, of Holland and Britain.

Laservision, also a Philips development, while technically more advanced than any, can only play-back and not record on a home video machine, so has not been so successful.

# ══ Water-closet – *Lavatory* ══

The godson of Queen Elizabeth I, Sir John Harrington, invented a water-closet for his own house at Kelston, near Bath, in 1589.

Queen Elizabeth I ordered one for her own use at Richmond Palace. She was very impressed by it.

Much like a modern lavatory it had a cistern to hold the fresh water, a pan underneath, a handle (in the seat) to release the valve to make the water flow – and even the water running through specially-designed channels to clean the whole of the bowl.

The main difference was that it flushed into a cesspit instead of into a sewer.

It did not become popular for two main reasons – lack of a proper water supply to most houses, and no proper sewers or drains.

Sir John Harrington published a pamphlet describing it in 1586, but even that was no help.

The modern lavatory came about only after the invention of the ballcock or ballvalve in 1748. This consists of a hollow ball, which floats on water, fitted to the end of an arm.

As the water rises, so it closes the outlet to which the arm is attached. Even so, the first water-closet manufacturer was Joseph Bramah, who started production in England in 1778.

After Bramah – whose firm did not close until 1890 – many other manufacturers began production, especially in Victorian times (including Thomas Crapper, whose products became so well-known that people talked about 'going for a crap').

Jennings' Pedestal Vase won a gold medal

when it was shown at the 1884 Health Exhibition in London – and Jennings was the one who invented the oval toilet seat which is still the main shape in use today.

The first modern public lavatories containing water-closets was opened in Fleet Street, London, in 1852, for gentlemen only. One for ladies opened in Bedford Street, London, ten days afterwards.

The people responsible were Sir Samuel Peto, a building contractor who erected Nelson's Column in Trafalgar Square, and Sir Henry Cole (*see* CHRISTMAS CARD).

The charge was twopence 'for use of the basic amenities', and the idea was to make a profit! Unfortunately, only 82 people used them in 1852, despite 50,000 handbills being distributed to explain what the lavatories were for.

Despite this failure, in 1855 the first public lavatories owned by the City of London Corporation opened – at a charge of one penny.

It remained one penny until decimal currency was introduced into Britain in 1971. Of course, it was free for men if they just stood up! (*See* TOILET-PAPER).

# X-ray

William Rontgen was the director of the Physical Institute at Wurzburg, Germany.

In 1895 he was experimenting with electrical discharges through vacuum tubes when he noticed that while he was doing that, barium platino-cyanide which had been painted on to a piece of paper nearby began to glow, apparently by itself.

To prevent this happening again, he covered the discharge tube with cardboard, but the paper still glowed.

He knew then that he had discovered an invisible ray which could pass through objects.

Within a month his discovery was being talked about by Thomas Hunt, a famous British doctor of the time, as 'probably the greatest landmark in the whole history of diagnosis', because now it was obvious that a ray had been discovered which could be used to 'see' through a human body and so identify bone fractures and so on.

By using the ray on one side of a human body, and having a photographic plate on the other, a photograph of what was wrong could be seen.

Before long radiography, as it began to be called, and still is called, was a recognised process for use in hospitals.

# Zip-fastener

Whitcomb L. Judson, a Chicago engineer, devised two metal chains, which joined together as a slide passed over them, to take the place of the rows of buttons on high boots in 1893.

There were two faults in this invention which the public didn't like, however. Not only did the device catch on things as people walked past, but it came open too easily without warning.

A Swedish engineer, Gideon Sundback, working in Hoboken, New Jersey, USA, in 1913, came up with a simple but brilliant solution to the problems of Judson's slide fastener. He made his units in pairs, on two parallel tapes of cloth.

Each tooth on the zip was really a hook which hooked into an eye *under* the hook on the same place on the opposite tape. The slide pressed out the teeth as it ran over them and left them hooked together. This is still how a zip-fastener works.

When America entered the First World War in 1917, the American armed forces ordered the new invention to be fitted on to uniforms, flying clothes, and so on.

In Britain, manufacture began in 1919 under the name of The Ready Fastener, by the firm of Kynoch, of Birmingham.

Its real success came, though, when it was demonstrated at the Empire Exhibition at Wembley in 1924. At that exhibition a fastener was zipped and unzipped three million times without breaking down.

How it got its modern name happened in 1926, when the writer Gilbert Frankau fiddled with one and said: 'Zip! it's open. Zip! it's closed.' Ever since then, it's been known as the zip-fastener.

The first women's clothes to have zips were designed by Madame Schiaparelli, a famous Parisian clothes designer, in 1930.

Until then, zips were regarded as improper for women to use on their dresses. That was perhaps a little odd, because the first zips on men's trousers were not introduced until 1935.